GCSE

Oxford Literature Companions

The Sign of Four

Arthur Conan Doyle

KINGSTHORPE COLLEGE
ENGLISH DEPARTMENT

WORKBOOK

Notes and activities: Annie Fox
Series consultant: Peter Buckroyd

OXFORD
UNIVERSITY PRESS

Contents

Introduction

What are Oxford Literature Companions?

Oxford Literature Companions is a series designed to provide you with comprehensive support for popular set texts. You can use the Companion workbook alongside your novel, using relevant sections during your studies or using the workbook as a whole for revision. The workbook will help you to create your own personalized guide to the text.

What are the main features within this workbook?

Each workbook in the Oxford Literature Companion series follows the same approach and includes the following features:

Activities

Each workbook offers a range of varied and in-depth activities to deepen understanding and encourage close work with the text, covering characters, themes, language and context. The Skills and Practice chapter also offers advice on assessment and includes sample questions and student answers. There are spaces to write your answers throughout the workbook.

Key quotation

Key terms and quotations

Throughout the workbook, key terms are highlighted in the text and explained on the same page. There is also a detailed glossary at the end of the workbook that explains, in the context of the novel, all the relevant literary terms highlighted.

Quotations from the novel appear in blue text throughout this workbook.

Upgrade

As well as providing guidance on key areas of the novel, throughout this workbook you will also find 'Upgrade' features. These are tips to help with your exam preparation and performance.

Progress check

Each chapter of the workbook ends with a 'Progress check'. Through self-assessment, these enable you to establish how confident you feel about what you have been learning and help you to set next steps and targets.

Which edition of the novel has this workbook used?

Quotations have been taken from the Oxford University Press edition of *The Sign of Four* (ISBN 978-019-835535-9).

Plot and Structure

The Sign of Four by Arthur Conan Doyle is a **novel** featuring the detective Sherlock Holmes who must solve a mystery involving a range of exciting characters and many puzzling events. The novel is told from the point of view of the **narrator**, Dr Watson, Sherlock Holmes's friend and chronicler.

The **plot** of the novel consists of its main events. The order of events is particularly important in mystery or detective fiction when the author must consider how to create tension and when to reveal key clues.

narrator a person or character who tells a story

novel a lengthy piece of prose fiction that usually uses character and action to convey its narrative

plot the events or storyline of a narrative

Order of events

Activity 1

Plot events from the first chapter have been listed below but in the wrong order.

a) Write numbers in the boxes next to each event to indicate the correct order.

b) Write three sentences below explaining why you think Conan Doyle ordered the first chapter in this way.

Mrs Hudson announces a visitor   - - - - - - -

Holmes explains that he is easily bored   - - - - - - -

Holmes injects himself with cocaine   - - - - - - -

Holmes detects the origins of Watson's watch   - - - - - - -

Watson criticizes Holmes for risking his powers   - - - - - - -

Holmes describes a recent case he completed for the French detective service   - - - - - - -

Conan Doyle may have chosen to order the events in this order so as to

- -

- -

- -

- -

- -

Upgrade

Although you must show that you understand the plot of the novel, you will never be asked simply to retell it. When looking at the plot of the first chapter, consider what we learn about the main characters before the main mystery of *The Sign of Four* gets properly under way.

Keeping track of the plot

Activity 2

As you read the novel, keep track of the main events by creating a table like the one below.
For this activity, complete the empty squares in the table.

Chapter	Key plot points	Key quotations	Effect on the reader
1	Introduction of Holmes and Watson.		Reader learns of Holmes's powers. The contrasting characters of Watson and Holmes are established.
2	Miss Mary Morstan explains the baffling case of the disappearance of her father and the mysterious annual gift of a pearl. She asks for Holmes and Watson to accompany her to a meeting.	"He disappeared upon the 3rd of December, 1878 – nearly ten years ago." 'What an attractive woman!'	The reader learns the first clues to the mystery. Watson's attraction to Mary Morstan is contrasted with Holmes's apparent indifference.
3		'Four years later Sholto dies. Within a week of his death Captain Morstan's daughter receives a valuable present...' '...a curious hieroglyphic...' 'The sign of the four...'	
4	Introduction to Thaddeus Sholto. He tells of his father's deathbed confession involving hiding the death of Captain Morstan and his desire to make reparation.		
5			

Narration

The novel has a **first person narrator**, Watson. This means that the reader experiences the events of the novel solely from his perspective. It would be a very different novel if it was written from the first person point of view of Sherlock Holmes or by an **omniscient third person narrator**.

first person narrator
a narrator who is usually one of the characters in the novel and writes about events from a single perspective, using the word 'I'

omniscient third person narrator an all-knowing narrator who can relate the thoughts and feelings of many characters, usually in the third person

Activity 3

Read the paragraph beginning: '**I was annoyed at this criticism of a work which had been specially designed to please him.**' *(Chapter 1)*

In your notebook, rewrite the paragraph with Sherlock as the narrator.
You could begin with: 'Watson was annoyed at this criticism of his work which had been specially designed to please me. Watson was, I suspect, irritated by my egotism…'

Activity 4

Now complete the paragraph below, explaining how the choice of narrator influences your experience of the book in terms of establishing tension and characterization.

Conan Doyle chose to make Watson his narrator because

Upgrade

Rather than just identifying Watson as the narrator, try to consider the effect of his narration on the reader. For example, when is it helpful to delay the resolution of the plot because both he and the reader at times are ignorant of Holmes's thoughts?

Exposition

Part of a writer's craft is to tell us about the characters' backgrounds, the setting or events that may have occurred before the main action of the plot. This is called **exposition** and skilful writers weave it seamlessly into their narrative without interfering with the action.

> **exposition** description and explanation of ideas, usually used in the first part of a novel when characters and themes are introduced, but also used elsewhere, for example to give background information

Activity 5

Read the quotations below from the novel and complete the table to explain what information about the characters' pasts has been provided by Conan Doyle. Then in your notebook record further examples of exposition that complete the background to the novel.

Character	Example of exposition	What we learn about the character/ characters
Major Sholto	"Our father would never tell us what it was he feared, but he had a most marked aversion to men with wooden legs. On one occasion he actually fired his revolver at a wooden-legged man, who proved to be a harmless tradesman canvassing for orders. We had to pay a large sum..." (Spoken by Thaddeus Sholto, *Chapter 4*.)	This suggests that Major Sholto was haunted by something in his past. He was afraid, sometimes resorting to violence, and used his money to solve problems.
Captain Morstan	"In the year 1878 my father, who was senior captain of his regiment, obtained twelve months' leave and came home. He telegraphed to me...His message, as I remember, was full of kindness and love." (Spoken by Mary Morstan, *Chapter 2*.)	Captain Morstan was a high ranking military man. Returning on leave to England he contacts his daughter with an affectionate message. This makes his subsequent disappearance all the more mysterious as there is no hint of a problem in this account.
Sherlock Holmes	"Yes, I have been guilty of several monographs. They are all upon technical subjects." (Spoken by Holmes, *Chapter 1*.)	
Jonathan Small	"I am a Worcestershire man myself, born near Pershore. I dare say you would find a heap of Smalls living there now if you were to look...They were all steady, chapel-going folk...while I was always a bit of a rover." (Spoken by Jonathan Small, *Chapter 12*.)	

Conflict

Holmes is the **protagonist** of the novel who, in addition to his many impressive skills, is also presented as a flawed character. Even his good friend Watson has criticisms of him. In the opening chapter there are at least three sources of **conflict** between Holmes and Watson that may reflect badly on Holmes:

conflict when characters have opposing desires or objectives

protagonist the central character in the novel

- Holmes's use of drugs

- Holmes's lack of appreciation for Watson's writing

- Holmes's apparent heartlessness in exposing the sad history of Watson's brother.

Activity 6

Read the following excerpts from Watson's account in Chapter 1 of his annoyance with Holmes, annotating any words or phrases that suggest sources for conflict.

'...I had become more irritable at the sight, and my conscience swelled nightly within me at the thought that I lacked the courage to protest.'

Suggests that Watson is a moral person who has a sense of duty.

He may worry about offending Holmes.

"Why should you, for a mere passing pleasure, risk the loss of those great powers with which you have been endowed?"

'I was annoyed at this criticism of a work which had been specially designed to please him.'

'"This is unworthy of you, Holmes," I said.'

Activity 7

Answer the following question:

'What do we learn about the relationship between Holmes and Watson in the opening chapter of the novel?'

Remember to locate the differences between the characters and the potential for conflict between them.

The structure of detective fiction

The Sign of Four is an example of detective fiction. The typical structure of detective fiction is:

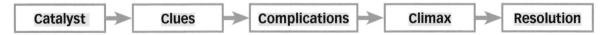

Catalyst → Clues → Complications → Climax → Resolution

The catalyst is the initial event that starts the investigation. In the case of *The Sign of Four*, the catalyst is Mary Morstan asking for Holmes's help in solving her mystery.

Activity 8

Now complete the structure flow chart below by adding the events in the novel that you think best fit each heading.

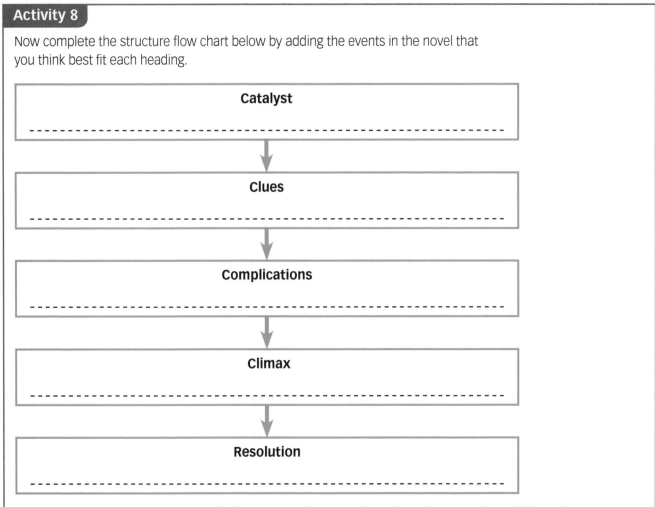

Catalyst

↓

Clues

↓

Complications

↓

Climax

↓

Resolution

----

catalyst something that causes an event
climax the most exciting and tense section of the novel, which usually occurs near the end
clue evidence used in the detection of crime
complication plot or character detail that makes a straightforward solution more difficult
resolution the point in the story where the mystery or problem of the story is solved or brought to a conclusion

Sub-plot

In addition to the main plot that involves solving the mystery, there is also the **sub-plot** focusing on the romance between Mary and Watson.

> **sub-plot** a second plot that runs alongside the main plot

Activity 9

a) Use the chart to trace the development of this sub-plot by noting the changes in intensity in the relationship between Mary and Watson.

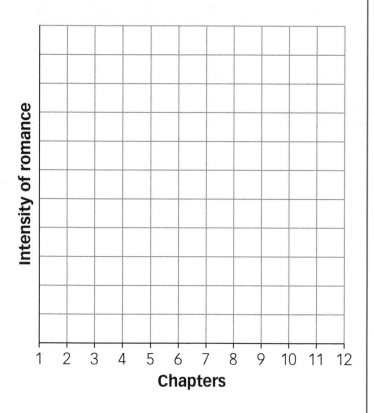

b) List the complications that get in the way of the relationship.

----

c) Write a bullet point list of your ideas about the importance of the sub-plot.

Timescale

The action of the novel takes place over a mere four days and the compressed nature of this timescale adds to the story's pace and excitement.

Activity 10

Use the timeline below to chart the key events of the novel (a few have been put in to get you started).

Day 1	Day 2	Day 3	Day 4
Watson and Holmes at Baker St. Miss Morstan presents case.	The Baker Street Irregulars get their orders.		Boat chase.

Day or night?

Activity 11

a) In order to create a particular atmosphere, Conan Doyle sets some key scenes at night, whereas others occur in the morning or afternoon. Here is one student's analysis of the night-time setting in Chapter 3.

> The ominous atmosphere of the mysterious journey to Thaddeus Sholto's house is increased by its night-time setting. All the houses around it are described as 'dark' and the only sign that they are expected is a 'single glimmer' from the house. This makes the location seem isolated and forbidding.

b) Now read the quotation below from Chapter 10. How important is the time of day in this extract in terms of establishing tension or excitement?

'**She was still, however, well in view, and the murky uncertain twilight was settling into a clear, starlit night.**'

Don't just note if something occurs during the night or day, but consider the effect of when the scene is set. For example, how does Conan Doyle use the descriptions of night to increase the tension and atmosphere of key scenes?

Tension and suspense

The creation of **tension** and **suspense** is considered an essential element of a detective story.

Some ways of creating tension include:

- Compression of time: the characters are working to a tight deadline with the reader aware of the minutes ticking by.

- Setting: a location that suggests danger.

- Darkness: things being out of sight or only partly seen.

- Character flaw: an aspect of an important character that will mean they might fall easily into danger.

- Emotions: a character showing how tense or frightened he or she is.

- Mystery: setting up questions in the reader's mind that are not easy to answer.

- Red herrings: false clues that mislead the reader and encourage a false conclusion.

> **suspense** a state of uncertainty, perhaps awaiting a judgement or solution
>
> **tension** elements that make the reader feel worried, interested, fearful or excited

Activity 12

Look at some of the events in *The Sign of Four* and write a note below each one explaining how it contributes to the tension in the novel.

Bartholomew Sholto's murder takes place in a locked room.

The locked room makes it more puzzling – how has this seemingly impossible murder occurred?

The boat chase occurs at night.

Watson is sometimes ruled by his emotions rather than by logic, so can misread clues.

The story takes place over four days.

Pondicherry Lodge is described as a gloomy place with 'its deathly silence'.

Thaddeus Sholto is frightened and his 'teeth were chattering in his head' on the way to his brother's room.

Flashbacks

While most of the novel is Watson's **chronological** account of events, there are sections where other characters take over the tale, explaining their back stories, sometimes in the form of **flashbacks**. Both Mary Morstan and Thaddeus Sholto have lengthy sections in which they develop the story by offering background clues to the mystery. Most significantly, the majority of Chapter 12 is dedicated to Jonathan Small's telling of 'The Strange Story of Jonathan Small'.

chronological arranged in the order of time in which events occurred

flashback a narrative device in which the chronological order of the story is interrupted and events from an earlier time are presented

Activity 13

On the lines below write a paragraph explaining how the flashback to Small's story affects your appreciation of him as a character and your understanding of the plot. Cover the following points:

- Sympathy created for Small
- Understanding of Small's actions
- The resolving of any remaining mysteries.

Obstacles or complications

Despite the brilliance of Sherlock Holmes, it is important that he does not solve the mystery too quickly or there would be no novel. Part of the art of detective stories is to reveal the clues gradually, but also to keep the final solution unknown until the end. In order to delay the revelation, Conan Doyle employs a number of different techniques.

Activity 14

Look at the events and quotations below. Briefly explain how each prevents a quick solution to some of the mysteries presented in the story.

> Chapter 2: The mysterious letter to Mary Morstan: "No address." "Your unknown friend."

> Chapter 3: The evening carriage ride to meet the author of the letter: 'The sign of the four...' "No, I confess that I do not see how this bears upon the matter."
>
> 'The situation was a curious one. We were driving to an unknown place, on an unknown errand.'

> Chapter 6: The arrival of Athelney Jones: "You see that I am weaving my web round Thaddeus."

A surprising revelation

Activity 15

Unusually, Conan Doyle has Holmes reveal the name of the murderer halfway through the novel rather than at the end. Read the rest of Chapter 6 after the revelation and list all the questions you still have about the crime and who committed it.

Climax

The climax of a novel often occurs towards the end of the narrative and there is a sense that the story has been leading up to that point. In *The Sign of Four* the climax occurs in Chapter 10, with the exciting boat race, the death of Tonga and the capture of Small. Conan Doyle employs a number of techniques to make sure that the climax is exciting, tense and **fast-paced**.

> **fast-paced** moving or developing quickly

Activity 16

To analyse how Conan Doyle achieves a compelling climax to the novel complete the table below, providing examples from the text.

Technique	Example	Effect on reader
Mixing relative calm with sudden excitement	After a discussion, Holmes suddenly sees the *Aurora*. "And there is the *Aurora*," exclaimed Holmes, "and going like the devil!"	The reader realizes that the pace of the chapter is suddenly accelerating, moving from dialogue to action.
Quick-paced exciting action	"very fast," "If we burn the boat we must have them."	
High-stakes; what is happening is very important		
Obstacles are presented		
Characters are in mortal danger		

Activity 17

Below are some quotations from Chapter 10 that emphasize the speed of the action. Use these quotations and others from the chapter in a paragraph explaining how they contribute to the exciting climax of the novel.

'"Pile it on, men, pile it on!" cried Holmes…'

'We flashed past barges, steamers, merchant-vessels…'

'…both boats flying at a tremendous pace.'

Resolution

At the end of a detective novel, the reader expects the mystery to be solved. The various elements of the plot and sub-plot are brought together and resolved for the reader. Another name for this stage of the plot is the **denouement**. Some readers may find this section of the novel **anti-climactic** after the excitement of the action-filled climax. However, in order for the novel to satisfy the curiosity of the reader, it is important to understand the motivations of the characters and whether or not their objectives were achieved.

anti-climactic less important or exciting than the build-up or climax that has just taken place

circular structure a form that ends with phrasing or subject matter that recalls the beginning of the narrative

denouement the final part of a novel when the various strands of the plot are brought together and resolved

stock character easily recognized, familiar character that requires little development or insight

Activity 18

Use the headings in the spider diagram on the right to make notes about the resolution of the various strands of the plot, such as the reason for Major Sholto's death; who was responsible for Bartholomew Sholto's death; and the success of Watson's romance with Mary.

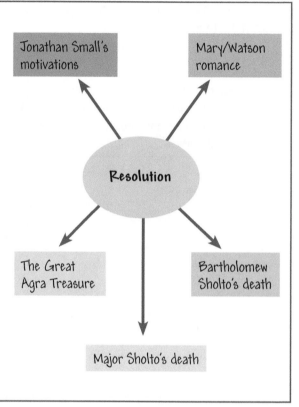

Jonathan Small's motivations

Mary/Watson romance

Resolution

The Great Agra Treasure

Bartholomew Sholto's death

Major Sholto's death

Circular structure

Activity 19

Some readers feel that the novel has a **circular structure** since it ends as it began with Holmes reaching for a cocaine bottle. Do you agree, or do you believe there have been significant changes in the lives of the characters at the end of the novel? Do the characters go on emotional journeys or are they **stock characters**, who remain unchanged by events? Write a bullet point list supporting your point of view.

When characters are introduced

One aspect of structure that an author must consider is when and how characters are introduced. The author Graham Greene wrote that the novel's opening chapter was 'perhaps the richest Doyle ever wrote', asking 'What popular author today could so abruptly introduce his hero as a drug addict without protest from his public?'

Activity 20

Use the table below to note when each of the following characters is introduced and what the effect of the introduction is.

Character	Chapter and key quotation	Effect on reader
Thaddeus Sholto		
Athelney Jones		
Jonathan Small	First named in Chapter 6 but not seen until Chapter 10. Tells his story in Chapter 12. "If you want to hear my story, I have no wish to hold it back. What I say to you is God's truth, every word of it."	

Character names

Another feature of Conan Doyle's writing is his choice of names. Graham Greene wrote, 'Here he [Conan Doyle] already shows his mastery of names, perhaps equalled only to Dickens: Pondicherry Lodge, Thaddeus and Bartholomew Sholto, the detective Athelney Jones, names which contrast so admirably with plain Doctor Watson and Mrs Hudson.'

Activity 21

Choose two names from the list above and write three sentences explaining what the names suggest to you about the characters.

Writing about structure

Activity 22

In order to write well about structure you need to be confident of the terminology.
Test yourself by matching each term to the correct definition:

Narrator	The central character in the novel
Climax	Something that causes an event
Catalyst	A person who tells a story
Chronological	Arranged in the order of time in which events occurred
Protagonist	The most exciting and tense section
Exposition	A second plot that runs alongside the main plot
Sub-plot	Explanation of background information

Activity 23

Using a selection of the terminology above, write two paragraphs in your
notebook answering the following question:

> 'How does the structure of *The Sign of Four* create excitement and interest in
> the story for the reader? Remember to include clear examples from the text.'

Including structure points in your answers

One of the most common mistakes is simply to retell the plot of the story rather
than to answer the question with an analysis of the plot and structure.

Activity 24

Read this students' answer to the question below and highlight any examples of:

- literary terminology
- analysis of why the author has structured the story this way.

> 'What is the importance of the character Jonathan Small in the novel?'

Although Jonathan Small is a major character in the novel and, at least on
first impressions, the novel's antagonist, his name is only first mentioned
in Chapter 6. For a detective story, it is surprising that the culprit is named so
early, but Conan Doyle expands the goal of his detection beyond discovering the
thief's identity to preventing Small's escape with the treasure and unearthing
his motivations. The denouement of the novel, Chapter 12, allows Small a first
person narrative of his adventures. Perhaps surprisingly the reader gains some
sympathy for him as a character as he is shown to have committed some crimes,
but also to have some honour.

When writing about structure, here are some tips:

- Consider when in the novel an event occurs – whether it is in the beginning, middle or end or before or after a significant event.
- Use terminology like: climax, resolution, protagonist, conflict.
- Consider how devices like narration or flashbacks affect the reader's experience of the novel.
- If appropriate, reflect on the importance of the sub-plot.
- Analyse how the novel adheres to the demands of detective fiction.

 ## Progress check

Use the chart below to review the skills you have developed in this chapter. For each column, start at the bottom box and work your way up towards the highest level in the top box. Tick the box to show you have achieved that level.

I can use well-integrated textual references from *The Sign of Four* to support my interpretation ☐	I can analyse the effects of Conan Doyle's use of language, structure and form in *The Sign of Four*, using subject terms judiciously ☐
I can use quotations and other textual references from *The Sign of Four* to support my explanation ☐	I can explain how Conan Doyle uses language, structure and form to create effects in *The Sign of Four*, using relevant subject terms ☐
I can make references to some details from *The Sign of Four* ☐	I can identify some of Conan Doyle's methods in *The Sign of Four* and use some subject terms ☐
Textual references	**Language, structure, form**

Context

It will enrich your understanding of the novel if you appreciate the context in which it was first read, including the life of the author, the social and historical environment and the literature of the age.

Arthur Conan Doyle

Activity 1

Below are some key facts about Arthur Conan Doyle. Highlight any points that help your understanding of the context in which the novel was written.

- Conan Doyle was born in Edinburgh in 1859.
- While studying medicine, Conan Doyle met Dr Joseph Bell, who inspired aspects of the character of Sherlock Holmes.
- Conan Doyle was a doctor and first wrote fiction to supplement his income.
- The first Sherlock Holmes tale was *A Study in Scarlet* published in 1887.
- Conan Doyle wrote *The Sign of Four* to be published in *Lippincott's Magazine* in 1890.
- The original titles Conan Doyle considered were 'The Sign of Six' or 'The Problem of the Sholtos'.
- Conan Doyle did not know London well when he wrote this novel and worked largely from maps rather than first-hand experience.
- Conan Doyle had an interest in the scientific developments and philosophical arguments of his day.
- Conan Doyle was a prolific writer who, in addition to the Sherlock Holmes stories, wrote historical novels and plays.
- Conan Doyle was a passionate advocate of justice and worked on two cases helping to exonerate people who had been wrongly accused of crimes.
- Conan Doyle admired the writing of Edgar Allan Poe, who wrote one of the earliest detective novels.

Using the information above, complete the following sentence:

Conan Doyle's background influenced the writing of 'The Sign of Four' because

----

Upgrade

It is important to be clear that although both Watson and Conan Doyle were doctors, they aren't the same person. However, Conan Doyle has created a doctor narrator who may share some of his attributes, such as his knowledge of science.

Inspiration for Sherlock Holmes

An inspiration for Sherlock Holmes was Dr Joseph Bell, one of Conan Doyle's professors at the medical school he attended.

Activity 2

Read Conan Doyle's description of Dr Joseph Bell and then answer the questions that follow (some key phrases have been highlighted to assist you).

> Sherlock Holmes is the literary embodiment, if I may so express it, of my memory of a professor of medicine at Edinburgh University, who would sit in the patients' waiting-room with a face like a Red Indian and diagnose the people as they came in, before even they had opened their mouths. He would tell them their symptoms, he would give them details of their lives, and he would hardly ever make a mistake. 'Gentlemen,' he would say to us students standing around, 'I am not quite sure whether this man is a cork-cutter or a slater. I observe a slight callus, or hardening, on one side of his thumb, and that is a sure sign he is either one or the other.' His great faculty of deduction was at times highly dramatic. 'Ah!' he would say to another man, 'you are a soldier, a non-commissioned officer [NCO] and you have served in Bermuda. Now how did I know that, gentlemen? He came into our room without taking his hat off, as he would go into an orderly room. He was a soldier. A slight authoritative air, combined with his age, shows he was an NCO. A slight rash on the forehead tells me he was in Bermuda, and subject to a certain rash known only there.' So I got the idea for Sherlock.
>
> Conan Doyle, 1892 interview

a) What specific characteristics has Conan Doyle borrowed from Dr Bell in order to create Sherlock?

----

b) From this passage, give an example of Dr Bell's powers of observation.

----

c) How does Dr Bell's wide-ranging knowledge assist him in making conclusions?

----

d) Now compare Dr Bell's deductions with Sherlock's about Watson's brother in Chapter 1 and Jonathan Small in Chapter 6.

The Victorian era

Activity 3

a) From your own research and understanding of the Victorian era, match the correct answer to each question.

Question	Answer
Who was the reigning monarch when the novel was written?	India, Australia and South Africa
When did Jack the Ripper first strike?	221B Baker Street
What is a hansom cab?	1888
Where does Sherlock Holmes have his rooms?	Victoria
Where does much of the English action of *The Sign of Four* take place?	London Fog
What combination of weather conditions and pollution is described by Watson?	London
What was the most populated city in the world at this time?	London suburbs
How many miles of territory were said to be included in the British **Empire**?	A single-horse carriage
What were some of the countries in the British Empire?	14 million square miles

b) Are the following statements true or false? Add your answers to the table.

Statement	True or false?
Conan Doyle tired of writing Sherlock Holmes stories and tried to kill his creation off.	
The Indian Mutiny (also known as the Great Rebellion) took place in 1857–1859.	
Queen Elizabeth was ruling during the Victorian period.	
Conan Doyle met the writer Oscar Wilde.	
The Victorian era lasted until 1954.	
Women had the right to vote in the Victorian era.	

Empire a group of countries ruled over by a monarch or other single power

Detective fiction: The role of the detective

Activity 4

Read the following from the introduction of *The Suspicions of Mr Whicher* by Kate Summerscale about a real Victorian murder committed in 1860 and answer the questions in your notebook.

> A detective was a recent invention. The first fictional sleuth, Auguste Dupin, appeared in Edgar Allan Poe's 'The Murders in the rue Morgue' in 1841, and the first real detectives in the English-speaking world were appointed by the London Metropolitan Police the next year...A Victorian detective was a **secular** substitute for a prophet or a priest. In a newly uncertain world, he offered science, conviction, stories that could organise chaos. He turned brutal crimes – the vestiges of the beast in man – into intellectual puzzles. ...The scene he uncovered aroused fear (and excitement) at the thought of what might be hiding behind the closed doors of other respectable homes.

How can you relate this sentence to Holmes's behaviour?

How well does this describe Holmes's actions in Chapter 6?

What hidden secrets are revealed about Pondicherry Lodge?

secular non-religious, not associated with spiritual matters

Activity 5

a) The story by Poe mentioned above is narrated by a friend of the detective Auguste Dupin. Read Dupin's description of the police below and highlight any similarities with the depiction of the police in *The Sign of Four*.

> 'We must not judge of the means,' said Dupin, 'by this shell of an examination. The Parisian police, so much extolled for acumen, are cunning, but no more. There is no method in their proceedings, beyond the method of the moment. They make a vast parade of measures; but, not unfrequently, these are so ill adapted to the objects proposed, as to put us in mind of Monsieur Jourdain's calling for his robe-de-chambre – pour mieux entendre la musique.[1] The results attained by them are not unfrequently surprising, but, for the most part, are brought about by simple diligence and activity.'
>
> [1]Asking for his dressing gown in order to enjoy listening to music.

b) Using the information above, finish this sentence:

The attitude towards detectives at this time

Detective stories and the Empire: *The Moonstone*

The Moonstone (1868) by Wilkie Collins was a popular detective novel that shares a number of features with *The Sign of Four*. The Moonstone of the title refers to a diamond that is the source of the novel's mystery.

> **synecdoche** a figure of speech in which part of something is used to represent the whole, such as 'The ominous boots approached the door', meaning the soldiers who were wearing the boots

Activity 6

Read the following account of *The Moonstone* by Cannon Schmitt and think about any similarities with *The Sign of Four*. Then answer the questions below:

> Centred on an Indian diamond looted by a British Army officer during the Siege of Seringapatam, a historic battle for British control of India, *The Moonstone* moots the question of the effects of empire at home. As Franklin Blake [a character in the novel] exclaims about a country estate: 'When I came here from London with that horrible Diamond…I don't believe there was a happier household in England than this. Look at the household now! Scattered, disunited – the very air of the place poisoned with mystery and suspicion!'…A **synecdoche** for all imperial commodities, the Moonstone's overwhelming beauty is matched only by the overwhelming disturbance of English domestic life to which it gives rise.
>
> The diamond in *The Moonstone* reflects the function of empire in the production of wealth.

a) How was the Moonstone obtained?

----

b) What effect has it had on its new owners?

----

c) What similarities do you see between this plot and that of *The Sign of Four*?

The Aesthetic Movement

Thaddeus Sholto was modelled on followers of the **Aesthetic Movement**.

> **Aesthetic Movement** an arts movement in the latter half of the 19th century that promoted 'art for art's sake'. Followers favoured highly decorative objects and were often influenced by exotic artefacts from abroad being brought into Europe at the time
>
> **decadent** in a state of moral decline; self-indulgent

Activity 7

Look at the image of a recreation of an Aesthetic Movement room from the late 19th century:

a) Circle the words you would use to describe this room.

Beautiful   Exotic   Ornate   Comfortable

Bold   Conventional   Elaborate

b) Read the description of Thaddeus Sholto's room in Chapter 4 and make a list of any similarities between the room pictured opposite and his room.

- Oriental vase

The Aesthetic Movement believed that art should be decorative rather than useful or promoting any social or political meaning. Followers also promoted Eastern arts, which might have been considered sensual and **decadent** by more conservative members of Victorian society.

Activity 8

Consider what you learn about Thaddeus Sholto in Chapter 4 and then complete the following paragraph:

Conan Doyle appears to present Thaddeus Sholto as a comment on followers of the

Aesthetic Movement. He is shown to be

Victorian London

Most of *The Sign of Four* takes place in London and its suburbs. Conan Doyle's description of the busy metropolitan area differs from the newer residential suburbs in which Mrs Forrester and Thaddeus Sholto reside or the working class areas where Mr and Mrs Smith and Mr Sherman live and work.

Activity 9

Complete the table below to help you compare the different locations in the novel.

Location	Key quotations	Importance to novel
Baker Street (London)		
Lyceum Theatre (London)		
Thaddeus Sholto's home (Stockwell – suburban)		
Mrs Forrester's home (Lower Camberwell – considered suburban in the 19th century)		
Mr Sherman's home (Lambeth – London)		
Mr and Mrs Smith's home (Nine Elms – outer London)		

Modes of transportation

Activity 10

The two main forms of transportation in the novel are boats and hansom cabs. Compare one of the hansom cab journeys with the boat chase in Chapter 10.

You might begin with: 'Journeys are important in the novel. For example...'

The British Empire

When *The Sign of Four* was written, the British Empire was still expanding, with British people commonly believing that they were civilizing other countries by spreading British beliefs and values. The relationship between Britain and the colonies was often complicated. For British subjects the colonies were considered a source of riches and adventure, but were also associated with danger and, in some cases, imprisonment. For those being colonized, there was often anger at being exploited and dominated.

Activity 11

The Sign of Four explores different degrees of influence of the Empire. Complete the spider diagram below by adding quotations from *The Sign of Four* that show the influence of the Empire in the novel.

Wealth: "...how my folk would stare when they saw their ne'er-do-weel coming back with his pockets full of gold moidores." (Chapter 12)

Adventure

Empire

Imprisonment

Military action

The Indian Mutiny or Indian Rebellion of 1857

A key historic event featured in the novel is the Indian Mutiny, now more frequently called the Indian Rebellion, of 1857–1859. The British East India Company, which at one point was said to have accounted for half of the world's trade, controlled large areas of India. A rebellion began among the Sepoys or private soldiers as a result of a combination of factors, including insensitivity to their religious beliefs and harsh treatment by their superior officers. Agra, one of the settings of the novel, was one of the centres of this unrest.

Activity 12

Read the description in Chapter 12 that explains the reasons why the rajah sent his wealth with his servant, and then complete the following sentence:

Conan Doyle has used the historic event of the Great Rebellion in his plot by

----

Conan Doyle was writing with the preconceptions and prejudices of his age. For example, compare the lack of differentiation between the Indian characters in Chapter 12 to the development of the various English characters.

Activity 13

Complete the table below to note and analyse the descriptions of the key Indian characters.

Character	Key quotations	Analysis
Abdullah Khan	'the taller and fiercer of the pair'	A sense of threat?
Mahomet Singh		
Dost Akbar	'foster-brother'	
The 'merchant' Achmet		

Exploring locations: Foreign settings

Foreign locations were a staple feature in many Victorian novels as a source
of intrigue, mystery and sudden wealth.

diction choice of words

Activity 14

a) Read the descriptions below from Jonathan Small's adventures in Chapter 12 and
underline any words that make clear that the setting is not in England.

> "It is a dreary, fever-stricken place, and all beyond our little clearings
> was infested with wild cannibal natives…" *(Chapter 12)*

> "The beating of drums, the rattle of tomtoms, and the yells and howls
> of the rebels, drunk with opium and with bang…" *(Chapter 12)*

b) Throughout this chapter the **diction** used to describe the setting is specific to its
foreign location. From the words you have highlighted above, complete the
following paragraph:

Conan Doyle emphasizes the exotic location through his diction. Words like

_____

_____

The effect of this is

_____

_____

Activity 15

Look more closely at the
setting of Agra. Complete
the spider diagram, noting
how different aspects of
Agra are described in
the text.

Sights

Inhabitants

Sounds

Agra

Smells

Weather

Architecture

'driving rain', 'brown,
heavy clouds'

Women in Victorian literature

Mary Morstan is one of many governesses featured in Victorian literature. The role of a governess was one of the few acceptable forms of employment for educated, middle class women.

Activity 16

a) Read the bullet points below and choose several to include in an introductory contextual paragraph about Mary Morstan. Include quotations from *The Sign of Four* in your paragraph.

- Many women became governesses. The 1851 census showed that there were 25,000 employed as governesses in England.

- The role of a governess was to teach and look after the children of an upper class or upper-middle class family with whom they lived.

- Some felt that being a governess was a socially awkward and lonely role, as usually they were not accepted by employers as a social equal, yet they were thought to be 'above' the servants.

- Some women became governesses because of their family's sudden loss of money. It was considered a more 'genteel' occupation than working in a shop or as a seamstress.

- Domestic life was considered the appropriate sphere for women. Victorian women were sometimes idealized as 'The Angel in the House' – a perfect wife and mother, who sacrifices her own needs for those of her family.

----

b) Use the information above to complete the following paragraph:

Mary Morstan's social position in the novel is uncertain because

----

Victorian newspapers

Victorian newspapers often covered sensational and violent crimes.
The most famous of these cases involved Jack the Ripper, who was responsible
for at least five murders in London. His crimes started in 1888, two years before
The Sign of Four was published. The case remains unsolved and Conan Doyle
would have been aware of the many criticisms of the police and the contradictory
reporting in the newspapers.

Activity 17

Read the newspaper article in Chapter 8 and then answer the questions below.

a) Newspaper writing should cover 'Who?', 'What?', 'When?', 'Where?' and 'How?'
early in the article. Answer the following questions about the article in Chapter 8:

i Who? _____

ii What? _____

iii When? _____

iv Where? _____

v How? _____

b) Find at least two examples of word choices in this article that you would be
surprised to see in a 21st century newspaper.

i _____

ii _____

c) In your opinion, what aspects of this account of the burglary and death of
Bartholomew Sholto would have been particularly exciting to Victorian readers?

_____

_____

_____

Including context in your answers

Activity 18

The best responses embed context to explain how it assists an understanding of the novel, rather than simply listing facts and dates. Read these excerpts from three students' essays, all of which use context.

a) Underline every example of context in the extracts below.

b) Number the three essays from 1 to 3, based on how well they include the context to explain their ideas. (Note, the one with the most context, number 1, might not necessarily be the best answer: you are choosing the one that best uses context to offer insight into the novel.)

> Student 1: Arthur Conan Doyle was born in 1859 and was a doctor. He was writing during the Victorian age when Queen Victoria was the monarch. This is important because this is a Victorian novel, where people are riding in hansom cabs and women did not have many opportunities. Watson is a doctor and so was Conan Doyle, so perhaps that is why Watson is the narrator.

> Student 2: Mary Morstan's role in the action of the novel is, in many ways, limited by the expectations of women at this time. After the death of her father, she has become a governess, one of the few occupations available to middle class women at this time. However, she is an intelligent and admirable character (despite his scepticism about love, even Holmes says she is 'one of the most charming young ladies I ever met') and an appealing match for Watson in the novel's sub-plot.

> Student 3: Conan Doyle's attitudes towards Tonga and the Indian characters may be jarring or offensive to a modern reader; however, they are typical of many Victorians. The Indian Mutiny forms the background for Chapter 12 of the novel. The Mutiny took place in 1857–1859 and was a rebellion against the East India Company.

Activity 19

Choose one of the above paragraphs and, in your notebook, first improve and then continue the paragraph, including at least two more contextual references.

Activity 20

Test your ability to include context by answering one of the questions below in your notebook.

a) To what extent can Watson be viewed as a typical Victorian?

b) How have the events in India affected the lives of the characters in *The Sign of Four*?

c) To what extent can London be viewed as another character in this novel?

 Progress check

Use the chart below to review the skills you have developed in this chapter. For each column, start at the bottom box and work your way up towards the highest level in the top box. Tick the box to show you have achieved that level.

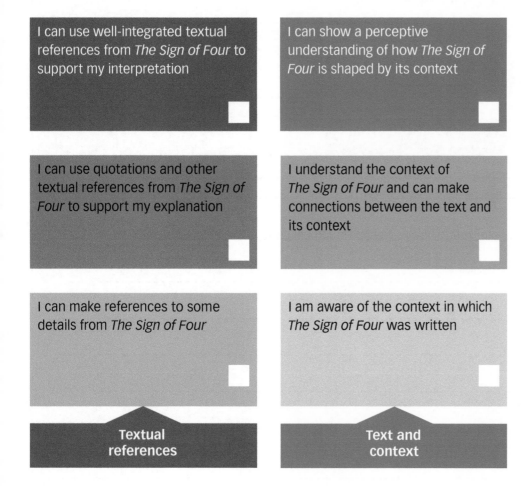

I can use well-integrated textual references from *The Sign of Four* to support my interpretation

I can show a perceptive understanding of how *The Sign of Four* is shaped by its context

I can use quotations and other textual references from *The Sign of Four* to support my explanation

I understand the context of *The Sign of Four* and can make connections between the text and its context

I can make references to some details from *The Sign of Four*

I am aware of the context in which *The Sign of Four* was written

Textual references

Text and context

First impressions of Sherlock Holmes

Sherlock Holmes is one of the most famous characters in fiction and has been depicted over the decades in many forms on stage, television and film.

Activity 1

Read the quotations below from the opening chapter. Then complete the 'what we learn' section about Sherlock Holmes.

What is written: 'the cool, nonchalant air of my companion' What we learn:

Watson notes the lack of emotions of his friend.
- -

What is written: 'His great powers, his masterly manner' What we learn:

- -

What is written: "But I abhor the dull routine of existence. I crave for mental exaltation." What we learn:

- -

What is written: '"It is simplicity itself," he remarked, chuckling at my surprise...' What we learn:

- -

Activity 2

Using the quotations above and others from the first chapter, complete the following paragraph:

My first impressions of Sherlock Holmes are
- -

- -

- -

- -

- -

- -

Activity 3

Now read a student's comment on Sherlock Holmes and decide what you agree or disagree with, and why.

From the opening pages, Sherlock Holmes declares that he is 'cold and unemotional' and yet there is evidence that he does have an emotional response to boredom. The lack of 'brain-work' leads to his drug use and he cries out against the 'dreary, dismal, unprofitable world', which suggests that he is unhappy rather than simply 'cold'. It is possible that a less admiring narrator than Watson would see these contradictions in Holmes's character.

Dr John Watson

Watson is a retired army surgeon who has become Holmes's friend and biographer. Although it is customary to think of Watson as a duller, more **staid** character than Holmes, Conan Doyle provides a number of indications that Watson has an interesting background.

> **staid** settled, unadventurous, conservative

Activity 4

Complete the table below in order to discover what the reader is told about Watson's past.

What he says	What this tells us about his past
"My constitution has not got over the Afghan campaign yet." *(Chapter 1)*	He has served in the army in Afghanistan where he was wounded.
"I even embodied it in a small brochure, with the somewhat fantastic title of 'A Study in Scarlet.'" *(Chapter 1)*	
"You have made inquiries into the history of my unhappy brother…" *(Chapter 1)*	
'In an experience of women which extends over many nations and three separate continents…' *(Chapter 2)*	
'What was I, an army surgeon with a weak leg and a weaker banking account…' *(Chapter 2)*	
'I have coursed many creatures in many countries during my checkered career, but never did sport give me such a wild thrill…' *(Chapter 10)*	

Activity 5

Using the information you have gathered about Watson, complete the spider diagram.

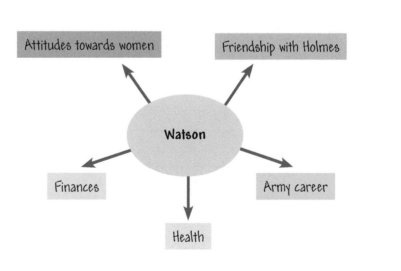

Contrasts

Holmes and Watson form one of the most famous partnerships in literature. Part of their appeal is the contrast between their two characters, which is set out in the first pages of the novel.

Activity 6

After reading the first two chapters, look at the adjectives below and select the three that you believe best describes each of the men and then provide evidence from the early chapters to support your ideas.

| Earnest | Bored | Disapproving | Pleasure-seeking | Respectable |

| Confident | Intelligent | Admiring | Sensitive | Brilliant | Trusting | Loyal |

| Self-centred | Stolid | Changeable | Restless | Logical | Emotional |

I believe Holmes is

- -

I think this because

- -

- -

- -

In my opinion, Watson is

- -

The evidence for this is

- -

- -

- -

Activity 7

As the novel progresses we learn Holmes's and Watson's opinions on many topics. Compare and contrast their views on these subjects using evidence from the text.

Topic	Holmes's opinion	Watson's opinion
Women/marriage		
Drug use		
Risk-taking		
Boredom		
Philosophy		
Emotions		

Descriptions of Holmes and Watson

One element of characterization is physical description. As the narrator, Watson has little opportunity to describe his own appearance, but he provides a number of physical descriptions of Holmes.

Activity 8

Read the following quotations and note what images they conjure for you.

Physical description of Sherlock Holmes	Explanation
'his clearcut, hawk-like features' *(Chapter 2)*	This bird imagery suggests a strong, predatory character.
'his long thin nose only a few inches from the planks and his beady eyes gleaming and deep-set like those of a bird.' *(Chapter 6)*	
'So swift, silent, and furtive were his movements, like those of a trained bloodhound...' *(Chapter 6)*	
'...his gaunt limbs, his earnest face, and the rise and fall of his bow.' *(Chapter 8)*	
'And he stretched his long white hand up for it. *(Chapter 12)*	

Activity 9

Instead of dwelling on his own physical appearance, Watson writes more about his own actions. Note your impressions of Watson from these quotations.

Description of Watson's actions	Explanation
'I picked up my hat and my heaviest stick...' *(Chapter 3)*	Wearing a hat observes the conventions of the day, as well as the awareness of the possible cold evening weather. Does he need the stick because of his limp or as a weapon?
'So we stood hand-in-hand, like two children...' *(Chapter 5)*	
'So shaken was [Thaddeus] that I had to pass my hand under his arm as we went up the stairs...' *(Chapter 5)*	
'I think I must have been rather over-acting my delight...' *(Chapter 11)*	

Characterization: How other characters react to Holmes

Who's talking?

Activity 10

One way that an author creates characterization is by showing what the characters say about each other. Look at the quotations below and decide whether it is Holmes speaking of Watson or Watson describing Holmes. Then beside each quotation explain what we learn about the characters from it.

"I had forgotten how personal and painful a thing it might be to you." *(Chapter 1)*

Holmes about Watson: Holmes acknowledges that he lacks emotions that Watson has.

"You really are an automaton – a calculating machine." *(Chapter 2)*

"Strange...how terms of what in another man I should call laziness alternate with your fits of splendid energy and vigour." *(Chapter 12)*

What makes Sherlock so special?

Activity 11

Read the following reactions to Sherlock:

"It's Mr Sherlock Holmes, the theorist. Remember you! I'll never forget how you lectured us all on causes and inferences and effects in the Bishopgate jewel case." *(Chapter 6)*

'"Mr Sherlock Holmes—" I began; but the words had a most magical effect, for the window instantly slammed down, and within a minute the door was unbarred and open... "A friend of Mr Sherlock is always welcome..."' *(Chapter 7)*

Explain how these reactions increase the mystique and appeal of the character of Sherlock Holmes.

Remember to write about the characters as constructs of the author and not as real people. Use phrases like 'Conan Doyle presents...' or 'The character of Holmes is shown to be...'.

Mary Morstan

Mary Morstan is the most significant female character in the novel and provides both the catalyst for the central mystery and the love interest in the sub-plot. In many ways she could be considered an idealized portrait of a young Victorian woman: sensitive, loving, refined, attractive and moral. Conan Doyle presents a character that is balanced between strength and gentleness; intelligence and modesty.

Activity 12

Read the following description of Mary from Chapter 2 and answer the questions.

'Miss Morstan entered the room with a firm step and an outward composure of manner. She was a blonde young lady, small, dainty, well gloved, and dressed in the most perfect taste. There was, however, a plainness and simplicity about her costume which bore with it a suggestion of limited means. The dress was a sombre greyish beige, untrimmed and unbraided, and she wore a small turban of the same dull hue, relieved only by a suspicion of white feather in the side. Her face had neither regularity of feature nor beauty of complexion, but her expression was sweet and amiable, and her large blue eyes were singularly spiritual and sympathetic… I have never looked upon a face which gave a clearer promise of a refined and sensitive nature.'

a) Why does Conan Doyle write 'outward' composure – what does this suggest to you?

----

b) What are 'limited means' and how might this affect how she dresses?

----

c) What does he find attractive about her eyes?

----

d) What does this description reveal about the describer, Watson?

Female characters

Besides Mary Morstan, there are several other female characters. Use the table below to note what we learn about them (in some cases you may have to write 'no evidence'). A few sections have been filled in to get you started.

	Mary Morstan	Mrs Hudson	Mrs Bernstone	Mrs Cecil Forrester	Mrs Smith
Physical appearance					
Importance to plot					Supplies information to Holmes
Typical dialogue					
Attitude towards danger/mystery	Brave, but also someone who turns to Watson for 'comfort and protection'		Terror: 'the shrill, broken whimpering of a frightened woman'	Excited, treats it like a work of fiction: 'It is a romance!'	
Role in Victorian society	Works as a governess – station in life lowered by absence of parents/fortune	'Worthy' landlady			

Considering the evidence from the table above, in your notebook, complete two paragraphs on the following topic:

> Conan Doyle presents Mary as the ideal woman for Watson. Compare and contrast the presentation of the character of Mary with that of at least two other female characters in the novel.

Thaddeus Sholto

Thaddeus Sholto is one of the most unusual characters in the novel. Inspired by followers of the Aesthetic Movement, such as Oscar Wilde, Conan Doyle has created in Thaddeus a character who is flamboyant, artistic and amusing. He is also shown to be a moral person with a conscience, as he is determined to return Mary's portion of her fortune to her.

> **eccentric**
> unconventional or unusual

Activity 15

Complete the unfinished notes below on Thaddeus Sholto with evidence from the text.

Physical appearance:

- Unconventional and unattractive, **'small,'** **'bald, shining scalp'** *(Chapter 4)*

- --

- --

Dialogue:

- **Eccentric**, large vocabulary, talkative, hypochondriac, sensitive to his own emotions but not always aware of the feelings of others: **"I am a great sufferer...Had your father, Miss Morstan, refrained from throwing a strain upon his heart, he might have been alive now."** *(Chapter 4)*

- --

- --

Habits:

- Smokes: **"I find my hookah an invaluable sedative."** *(Chapter 4)*

- Collects art: **"The landscape is a genuine Corot."** *(Chapter 4)*

- --

Importance to plot:

- Reveals death of Captain Morstan and Major Sholto. Knows about Agra treasure. Involves Mary in the story by contacting her: '**...he alone knew the fate of Arthur Morstan.**' *(Chapter 4)*

- --

- --

Twins: Thaddeus and Bartholomew Sholto

Activity 16

Although Thaddeus and Bartholomew Sholto are twins and physically resemble each other, they are shown to have quite different personalities. Complete the table below comparing the two characters.

	Thaddeus	Bartholomew
Introduction of character	After a secretive journey, a 'Hindoo servant' (Chapter 3) leads Sherlock, Watson and Mary to Thaddeus.	Described by Thaddeus as 'a clever fellows' (Chapter 4). Sherlock and Watson only see him after he has suffered a gruesome death.
Physical appearance		So resembles his twin that at first Watson thinks the dead man is Thaddeus: 'So like was the face to that of our little friend that I looked round at him...' (Chapter 5).
Surroundings	A deceptively ordinary terrace house with an exotic interior.	
Attitude towards treasure		
How others react to him		

Upgrade

Try to connect your understanding of the characters with the themes of the novel. For example, given how different the personalities are of the identical twins, what point might Conan Doyle be making about deceptive appearances? Victorians were interested in duality, when characters might encompass good and evil. How does the use of twins help Conan Doyle to explore this concept?

Jonathan Small

Jonathan Small is a fascinating **antagonist** for the novel. His life, as presented in Chapter 12, is like something out of an adventure novel.

Activity 17

Use the flow chart below to note the key events in Jonathan Small's life, accompanied by key quotations.

Beginnings

Boyhood in Worcestershire

Key quotations: _____

_____

↓

Complications

_____

Key quotations: _____

_____

↓

Adventures

Joins army

Key quotations: _____

_____

↓

Turning point

Loses leg

Key quotations: _____

_____

↓

Downfall

_____

Key quotations: _____

_____

Tonga

Tonga, the diminutive member of an indigenous Andaman Island tribe, is one of the most unusual characters in the novel. He is a character of fascination for others and is also shown to be a 'staunch and true' *(Chapter 12)* companion to Jonathan Small, assisting his escape.

Activity 18

Complete the spider diagram below by noting down the key things we know about Tonga.

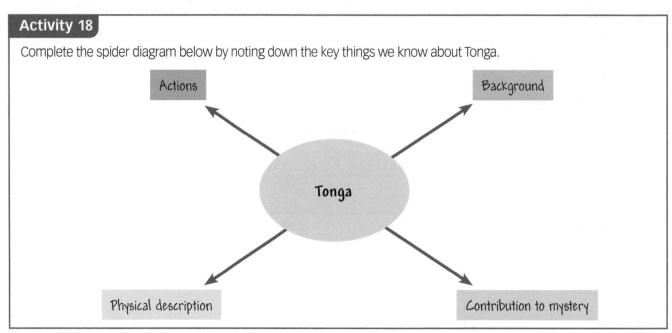

How others perceive Tonga

Activity 19

Tonga is perceived very differently by various characters. Read the quotations below and write a paragraph on what we learn about Tonga and the attitudes of English society at this time to people of his background.

"We earned a living at this time by my exhibiting poor Tonga at fairs and other such places as the black cannibal." *(Chapter 12)*

'...the unhallowed dwarf with his hideous face, and his strong yellow teeth gnashing at us...' *(Chapter 10)*

"They are a fierce, morose, and intractable people, though capable of forming most devoted friendships when their confidence has once been gained." *(Chapter 8)*

Major Sholto

Major Sholto, the father of Bartholomew and Thaddeus, is dead at the start of the novel, so the reader only learns about him from the account of others, including Mary, Thaddeus and Jonathan Small. Although Mary only knows him as a friend of her father's, Thaddeus and Small understood him better and have different opinions of him.

Activity 20

Look at the quotations below and label each one with 'Thaddeus' or 'Small' depending on who you think is describing Major Sholto.

"The villain Sholto went off to India..." *(Chapter 12)* _____

"All day he would wander about as black as thunder, and he took to drinking a deal more than was good for him." *(Chapter 12)* _____

"Never for an instant did we suspect that he had the whole secret hidden in his own breast..." *(Chapter 4)* _____

"I have only one thing," he said, "which weighs upon my mind...It is my treatment of poor Morstan's orphan." *(Chapter 4)* _____

"The scoundrel had stolen it all without carrying out one of the conditions..." *(Chapter 12)* _____

"He was very fearful of going out alone..." *(Chapter 4)* _____

"...only even as I looked at him his jaw dropped, and I knew that he was gone." *(Chapter 12)* _____

'When we returned...his head had dropped and his pulse had ceased to beat.' *(Chapter 4)* _____

Activity 21

Using the information you have collected about Major Sholto, write an answer to the following question:

'Major Sholto is, in many ways, the villain of the novel and proves that greed does not pay.' To what extent do you agree with this point of view? Use evidence from the text to support your ideas.

_____

_____

Captain Morstan

In Chapter 2, Mary presents her father's sudden disappearance as one of the great mysteries of the tale. Although Mary suggests he is a loving father, a more complex picture develops from the accounts of others.

Activity 22

Annotate the following excerpts, noting the positive and negative points about Captain Morstan.

> "My father was an officer in an Indian regiment, who sent me home when I was quite a child. My mother was dead, and I had no relative in England. I was placed, however, in a comfortable boarding establishment at Edinburgh, and there I remained until I was seventeen years of age. In the year 1878 my father, who was senior captain of his regiment, obtained twelve months' leave and came home. He telegraphed to me from London that he had arrived all safe, and directed me to come down at once, giving the Langham Hotel as his address. His message, as I remember, was full of kindness and love." *(Chapter 2)*

> "One night [Major Sholto] lost even more heavily than usual. I was sitting in my hut when he and Captain Morstan came stumbling along on the way to their quarters. They were bosom friends, those two, and never far apart. The major was raving about his losses.
>
> "'It's all up, Morstan,' he was saying as they passed my hut…
>
> "'Nonsense, old chap!' said the other, slapping him upon the shoulder. 'I've had a nasty facer myself, but—' That was all I could hear, but it was enough to set me thinking." *(Chapter 12)*

Activity 23

Use the spider diagram below to complete your impressions of Captain Morstan.

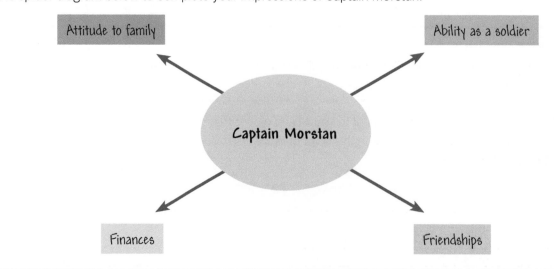

Minor characters

Conan Doyle enriches his novel by including a number of colourful minor characters, who each have a significant role or function.

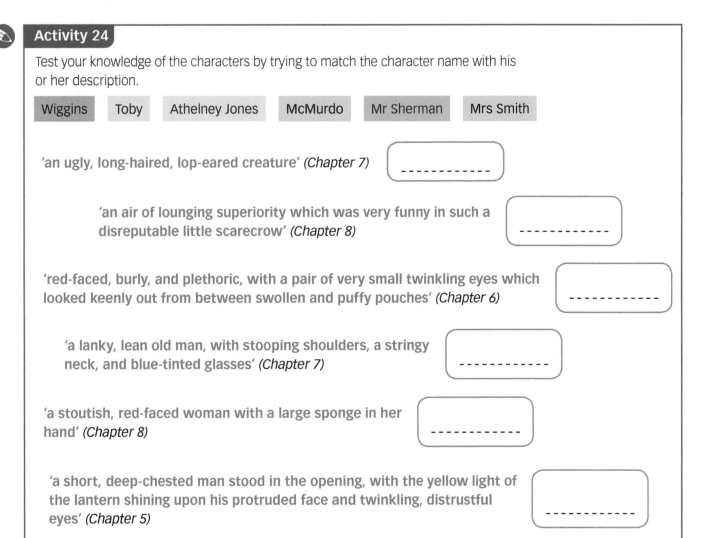

Activity 24

Test your knowledge of the characters by trying to match the character name with his or her description.

| Wiggins | Toby | Athelney Jones | McMurdo | Mr Sherman | Mrs Smith |

'an ugly, long-haired, lop-eared creature' *(Chapter 7)*
[_ _ _ _ _ _ _ _ _ _ _]

'an air of lounging superiority which was very funny in such a disreputable little scarecrow' *(Chapter 8)*
[_ _ _ _ _ _ _ _ _ _ _]

'red-faced, burly, and plethoric, with a pair of very small twinkling eyes which looked keenly out from between swollen and puffy pouches' *(Chapter 6)*
[_ _ _ _ _ _ _ _ _ _ _]

'a lanky, lean old man, with stooping shoulders, a stringy neck, and blue-tinted glasses' *(Chapter 7)*
[_ _ _ _ _ _ _ _ _ _ _]

'a stoutish, red-faced woman with a large sponge in her hand' *(Chapter 8)*
[_ _ _ _ _ _ _ _ _ _ _]

'a short, deep-chested man stood in the opening, with the yellow light of the lantern shining upon his protruded face and twinkling, distrustful eyes' *(Chapter 5)*
[_ _ _ _ _ _ _ _ _ _ _]

Activity 25

Read the following student's explanation of the importance of the minor characters in the novel. Then, in your notebook, write an improved version with more examples from the novel.

> Sherlock Holmes is shown to be able to deal effectively with a surprising range of characters. He has inspired a great deal of loyalty from characters like Mr Sherman and McMurdo. He also knows how to get Wiggins and the Baker Street Irregulars to do his bidding. In his conversation with Mrs Smith, he manages to prise from her a great deal of information without much effort. This suggests that he is knowledgeable about human psychology and what makes people tick.

'The Four'

'The Four' of the title are the four conspirators who take part in the murder and robbery. Two of the men are **'Sikh troopers'** *(Chapter 12)* or **'Punjaubees'** *(Chapter 12)* called Mahomet Singh and Abdullah Khan, who were under Small's command at the fort. The third was Dost Akbar, Khan's foster brother, who is accompanying the **'pretended merchant'** *(Chapter 12)* Achmet, who they are planning to rob. For his cooperation, Small becomes the fourth of the group and entitled to a quarter share of the treasure.

> **Upgrade**
>
> One way of analysing characters is to look at their relationships. How does the way Small behaves towards the Four contrast with how Sholto treats his colleagues?

Activity 26

Read the following section about 'the Four':

> "Then we solemnly renewed our oath to stand by each other and be true to our secret...We made careful note of the place, and next day I drew four plans, one for each of us, and put the sign of the four of us at the bottom, for we had sworn that we should each always act for all, so that none might take advantage. This is an oath that I can put my hand to my heart and swear that I have never broken." *(Chapter 12)*

a) How does Small emphasize the importance of the vow the four make?

----

b) Why do you think Small draws an image of the four of them?

----

c) Why does each of the four need a copy of the plan?

----

d) What does it say about Small that he is proud never to have broken this oath?

Writing about characterization

Use the checklist below in your revision of characters.

Have you considered:

- ☐ How and when the character is introduced?
- ☐ How the character's appearance is described?
- ☐ How characters may be perceived differently by other characters?
- ☐ How the character may provide a contrast to other characters?
- ☐ How the character may be defined by his or her relationship with other characters?
- ☐ How the character's dialogue may be distinctive and reveal aspects of his or her background?
- ☐ What the character's importance is in the development of the plot?
- ☐ If the character is well rounded or a stock, two-dimensional character?
- ☐ If the character might be perceived differently by a Victorian reader to a modern one?

Progress check

Use the chart below to review the skills you have developed in this chapter. For each column, start at the bottom box and work your way up towards the highest level in the top box. Tick the box to show you have achieved that level.

I can sustain a critical response to *The Sign of Four* and interpret the characters convincingly ☐	I can use well-integrated textual references from *The Sign of Four* to support my interpretation ☐
I can develop a coherent response to *The Sign of Four* and explain the characters clearly ☐	I can use quotations and other textual references from *The Sign of Four* to support my explanation ☐
I can make some comments on the characters in *The Sign of Four* ☐	I can make references to some details from *The Sign of Four* ☐
Personal response	**Textual references**

Narrative voice: Watson

Watson is the narrator of the novel and he has his own style of narration.

Activity 1

Look at the bullet points below and highlight those you most agree with.

- Watson's aspirations as a writer are clear from his particularly literary style of writing.
- Watson's narrative voice is one that is meant to encourage sympathy and identification from the reader.
- Watson uses a wide vocabulary that might challenge the average reader, but is in accord with his background as a doctor.
- Watson reveals not only the outward events of the novel, but also his internal, emotional struggle.
- Watson is the admiring mirror that reflects Sherlock Holmes.

Activity 2

Below is a section of Watson's musings from Chapter 2. Read the passage carefully and then answer the questions below.

'I sat in the window with the volume in my hand, but my thoughts were far from the daring speculations of the writer. My mind ran upon our late visitor – her smiles, the deep rich tones of her voice, the strange mystery which overhung her life…So I sat and mused until such dangerous thoughts came into my head that I hurried away to my desk and plunged furiously into the latest treatise upon pathology. What was I, an army surgeon with a weak leg and weaker banking account, that I should dare to think of such things? She was a unit, a factor – nothing more. If my future were black, it was better surely to face it like a man than to attempt to brighten it by mere will-o'-the-wisps of the imagination.' *(Chapter 2)*

a) How does this first sentence show that Watson is emotional rather than rational at this point?

----

b) Why does Watson quote Holmes when he says **'a unit, a factor'**?

----

c) What does Watson's choice of words in the final sentence demonstrate about his attitudes towards his position in the world?

Narrative voice: Jonathan Small

In Chapter 12, Jonathan Small takes over much of the narration and the tone and style of the novel shifts to accommodate this new voice.

Activity 3

Complete the spider diagram with more quotations that demonstrate the features of Jonathan Small's voice.

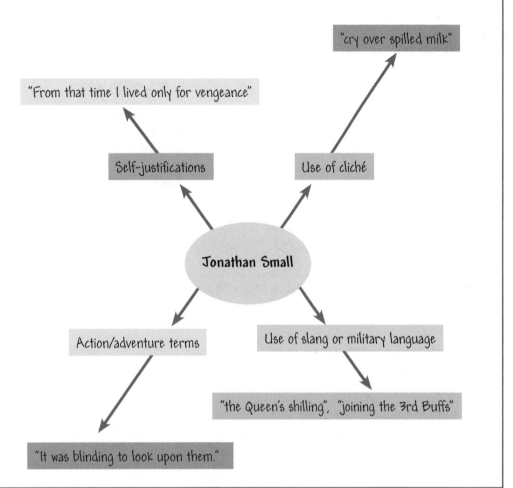

"From that time I lived only for vengeance"

"cry over spilled milk"

Self-justifications

Use of cliché

Jonathan Small

Action/adventure terms

Use of slang or military language

"the Queen's shilling", "joining the 3rd Buffs"

"It was blinding to look upon them."

Activity 4

Write in the space below, comparing the narrative voices of Watson and Jonathan Small and the different ways they tell their stories. Think about:

- the vocabulary used
- their attitudes towards crime
- what effect they hope their stories will have.

Simile

Part of Conan Doyle's (and therefore Watson's) literary style is to use a number of **similes** in order to make his story more vivid and interesting to the reader.

simile a comparison of one thing to another, using 'like' or 'as'

Activity 5

Complete the table below, which provides examples of Conan Doyle's use of similes. Remember to consider the effect that the choice of simile has on the reader.

Simile	Analysis
'...a bald, shining scalp which shot out from among it like a mountain-peak from fir-trees.' (Chapter 4)	This is a comic simile emphasizing Thaddeus's unconventional appearance. The surprising nature imagery adds to the humour as it is incongruous given the setting of Thaddeus's flat.
'So we stood hand-in hand, like two children, and there was peace in our hearts...' (Chapter 5)	
"It looks as though all the moles in England had been let loose in it." (Chapter 5)	
"Why, the house seems to be as full as a rabbit-warren!" (Chapter 6)	
'This Agra treasure intervened like an impassable barrier between us.' (Chapter 7)	
'...I could see him like an enormous glow-worm crawling very slowly along the ridge.' (Chapter 7)	
"The whole country was up like a swarm of bees." (Chapter 12)	

Activity 6

Read this extract from a student's essay. In your notebook, explain how you would develop this response and provide evidence from the text.

Conan Doyle uses similes for various effects. For example, some are comic and catch the reader by surprise, while others are more descriptive, helping the reader to picture the scene. Some of his similes are quite original, while others are more clichéd.

Remember that you must do more than just spot literary techniques; you must explain their effect. Upgrade

Metaphor

Metaphors are another way of making a comparison, but are often considered to be stronger than similes as the comparison is more direct.

> **metaphor** a comparison of one thing to another to make a description more vivid; unlike a simile, it does not use the words 'like' or 'as', but states that something is something else

Activity 7

Complete the table below to analyse the use of metaphors. Remember to consider the effect that the choice of metaphor has on the reader.

Metaphors	Analysis
"You really are an automaton – a calculating machine." *(Chapter 2)*	Watson uses the metaphor of a robot or a calculator to emphasize Holmes's unemotional nature. He is suggesting that Holmes is inhuman in his lack of feeling.
"A client is to me a mere unit, a factor in a problem." *(Chapter 2)*	
"You see that I am weaving my web round Thaddeus. The net begins to close upon him." *(Chapter 6)*	
"…the individual man is an insoluble puzzle, in the aggregate he becomes a mathematical certainty." *(Chapter 10)*	
'…but I could realize nothing save that the golden barrier was gone from between us.' *(Chapter 11)*	
'Whoever had lost a treasure, I knew that night that I had gained one.' *(Chapter 11)*	

Activity 8

How does Conan Doyle use similes and metaphors in order to convey to the reader the character of Sherlock Holmes?

Alliteration

Another technique that Conan Doyle uses is **alliteration**, which can make certain phrases more memorable, poetic or striking.

Activity 9

Look at the phrases below and complete the alliterative phrase by filling in the blank:

- **that wild, fierce _____'** *(Chapter 4)*
- **'long black shadows _____ backwards down the corridors'** *(Chapter 5)*
- **'swollen and puffy _____'** *(Chapter 6)*
- **'floated peacefully away upon a soft sea of _____'** *(Chapter 8)*
- **"...my watch was dark and ____, with a small _____ rain. It was _____ work..."** *(Chapter 12)*
- **"...you are a connoisseur of ____"** *(Chapter 12)*
- **'...her voice died away into a muffled _____'** *(Chapter 5)*

> When writing about alliteration, consider the effect of the repetitive sound. For example, are there soft **sibilant** 's' sounds that suggest breathing or falling asleep, or more **percussive** d's or t's that suggest something more aggressive or powerful?
>
> *Upgrade*

Activity 10

Look at this student's response and then find more examples from the novel to complete the paragraph.

There are a number of different effects created by Conan Doyle's use of alliteration. For example, he frequently uses repetitive 'd' sounds to recreate a depressing rainy atmosphere such as the 'dreary' and 'drizzly' day in Chapter 3, and the 'dark', 'dirty' and 'driving' rain in Chapter 12. The reader can imagine the heavy drops of rain with each repetition of that sound. However, other uses of alliteration are more comic or lyrical.

----

alliteration the use of the same first letter or sound in words that are next to one another or very closely grouped together

percussive related to drumming or striking

sibilant a speech sound that has a hissing sound such as that produced by saying 's' or 'sh'

Animal imagery

Activity 11

a) Conan Doyle uses animal imagery throughout the novel. Look at the imagery below and identify who is being described.

- "...strutting about as proud as a peacock" *(Chapter 12)* describes: _____
- "He could climb like a cat" *(Chapter 12)* describes: _____
- "...he rolled twice over like a shot rabbit" *(Chapter 12)* describes: _____
- '...like some evil fish' *(Chapter 10)* describes: _____
- '...like those of a trained bloodhound' *(Chapter 6)* describes: _____
- '...he broke out into a loud crow of delight' *(Chapter 6)* describes: _____
- '...his beady eyes gleaming and deep-set like those of a bird' *(Chapter 6)* describes: _____

b) Now complete the following sentence:

Conan Doyle uses animal imagery to emphasize some of the extraordinary qualities of his characters. For example,

_____

_____

_____

Anthropomorphism

Conan Doyle also gives human characteristics to some of the animals in the story, most notably Toby, the keen sniffer mongrel who assists with the search for the criminals.

> **anthropomorphism**
> attributing human characteristics to an animal or object

Activity 12

a) Read the following sentence from Chapter 7 and consider what human characteristics are being attributed to Toby.

'Then he waddled round in circles, looking up to us from time to time, as if to ask for sympathy in his embarrassment.' *(Chapter 7)*

_____

_____

b) Then read all of Chapter 7, making notes about Toby in your notebook under the following headings:

- Appearance
- Personality
- Importance to the novel

Dialogue and dialect/sociolect

Conan Doyle gives particular characteristics to the **dialogue** of his various characters, often giving indications of their:

- education
- social class
- geographical region
- personality
- occupation.

dialect particular pronunciations and word choices used by people of a specific geographical region

dialogue the speeches or conversations in a book or play

sociolect particular pronunciations and word choices used by people of a particular social class

Activity 13

Read the following extracts and make notes below about what the highlighted phrases reveal about the characters.

Thaddeus Sholto: "Have you your stethoscope? Might I ask you – would you have the kindness? I have grave doubts as to my mitral valve, if you would be so very good. The aortic I may rely upon, but I should value your opinion upon the mitral...I am a great sufferer, and I have long had suspicions as to that valve...Had your father, Miss Morstan, refrained from throwing a strain upon his heart, he might have been alive now." *(Chapter 4)*

Mr Sherman: "Don't mind that, sir; it's only a slowworm. It hain't got no fangs, so I gives it the run o' the room, for it keeps the beetles down. You must not mind my bein' just a little short wi' you at first, for I'm guyed at by the children, and there's many a one just comes down this lane to knock me up." *(Chapter 7)*

Activity 14

In your notebook, write a paragraph comparing the dialogue and characterization of Thaddeus and Mr Sherman.

Dialogue: Different registers

The dialogue in the novel also changes **register** depending on a variety of factors. For example, Watson speaks differently to Mary than he does to the male characters. Sherlock Holmes notably changes registers when he is in disguise, as in Chapter 9, or hiding his true intentions, such as his dialogue with Mrs Smith in Chapter 8.

register the choices of language dependent upon external factors such as occasion, audience and purpose

Activity 15

Read the dialogue below from Chapter 9 when Holmes is in disguise and then answer the questions below.

> "It was to him I was to tell it," he repeated with the petulant obstinacy of a very old man.
>
> "Well, you must wait for him."
>
> "No, no; I ain't goin' to lose a whole day to please no one. If Mr Holmes ain't here, then Mr Holmes must find it all out for himself. I don't care about the look of either of you, and I won't tell a word."
>
> He shuffled towards the door, but Athelney Jones got in front of him.
>
> "Wait a bit, my friend," said he. "You have important information, and you must not walk off. We shall keep you, whether you like it or not until our friend returns." *(Chapter 9)*

a) What is Watson's attitude to the 'old man'? How is Watson's register here different from how he speaks to other characters?

---

b) What does the use of non-standard English like 'ain't' suggest? What does his worry about losing 'a whole day' tell us about the man?

---

c) What does the old man's speech suggest about his attitude towards Holmes, Watson and Athelney?

---

d) Why does Athelney call him 'my friend'?

Media language

Conan Doyle also uses newspaper articles and advertisements to further the story. The writing style of these sections is distinctive from the rest of the novel. Although newspaper articles are meant to be factual, it is clear that these accounts are not entirely **unbiased**. Despite being written as an informative article, there is a **sensational** aspect to the account, with the use of **emotive language** and the flattering comments about Athelney Jones.

emotive language words chosen to encourage a certain emotion like sorrow or pity

sensational designed to excite or interest

unbiased impartial and lacking in prejudice; even-handed

Activity 16

Closely read the article in Chapter 8 and then complete the table below with examples from the text.

Factual	Sensational/Emotive	Flattery
'About twelve o'clock'	'Mysterious Business'	'single vigorous and masterful mind'

Irony

Conan Doyle uses **irony** to create humour in the novel, for example by pointing out the difference between the newspaper accounts of the crime and what has actually occurred. Sherlock Holmes sometimes uses **sarcasm** to express either his irritation or amusement at the ignorance or foibles of others. There is also irony in Watson knowing that if he succeeds in finding Mary's fortune, he will also, in his own mind and society's, become ineligible to be her husband. He is put in the ironic position of pursuing something which he believes will eventually work against his own self-interest.

> **irony** words that express the opposite of what is meant; the difference between what may be expected and what actually occurs; can also be used to make the reader or audience aware of something unknown to the characters
>
> **sarcasm** type of irony, using words to mean the opposite of what is said, often creating either a comic or insulting effect

Activity 17

Read the student's paragraph below and then write three more sentences to complete it.

Another way Sherlock Holmes's superiority is shown is through the use of irony. Although the newspaper articles in Chapters 8 and 9 praise Athelney Jones for his 'masterful mind' and 'trained and experienced faculties', the reader knows that this appraisal is false. In Chapter 6, Holmes has already announced the correct suspect, but Jones insists on arresting the wholly innocent Thaddeus. Watson even joins in the fun by sarcastically agreeing that they had a 'close shave' of being arrested themselves. Other examples of irony in the novel are...

Syntax

The writing in *The Sign of Four* is mainly formal, Standard English. The opening paragraph starts with the subject of the story 'Sherlock Holmes' and in complete sentences describes his chronological actions, finishing off the paragraph with a sentence that begins 'Finally', signalling the end of this sequence.

However, Conan Doyle experiments with different **syntax** at other points, such as longer sentences, and more surprising word orders. Some dialogue is written in informal, non-standard English and some sections are written in a **heightened** style to convey emotion.

heightened more elevated or intense

syntax the structure of sentences, including word order and grammar

Activity 18

Read the following extract from Chapter 5 and then answer the questions below.

> "A wondrous subtle thing is love, for here were we two, who had never seen each other before that day, between whom no word or even look of affection had ever passed, and yet now in an hour of trouble our hands instinctively sought for each other. I have marvelled at it since, but at the time it seemed the most natural thing that I should go out to her so, and, as she has often told me, there was in her also the instinct to turn to me for comfort and protection. So we stood hand-in-hand, like two children, and there was peace in our hearts for all the dark things that surrounded us." *(Chapter 5)*

a) What do you notice about the sentence length and use of punctuation in the first sentence?

----

b) What does the second sentence tell us about Watson's relationship with Mary?

----

c) How does the final sentence complete the depiction of love in this paragraph?

Sense of place: Buildings

Detective fiction often relies on locations to create a sense of mystery and intrigue.

In *The Sign of Four*, there are a number of distinctive environments ranging from Holmes's cosy rooms to the **Gothic horror** of Pondicherry Lodge; from Thaddeus Sholto's ornate rooms to the rugged fort in Agra.

> **Gothic horror** a genre of fiction that often revolves around a large, dark, frightening house and horrible secrets

Activity 19

Read the following descriptions of locations from the novel and answer the questions below for the first extract. Then answer the same questions for the next two extracts in your notebook.

- 'Inside, a gravel path wound through desolate grounds to a huge clump of a house, square and prosaic, all plunged in shadow save where a moonbeam struck one corner and glimmered in a garret window. The vast size of the building, with its gloom and its deathly silence, struck a chill to the heart.' *(Chapter 5)*

- 'As we drove away I stole a glance back, and I still seem to see that little group on the step – the two graceful, clinging features, the half-opened door, the hall-light shining through stained glass, the barometer, and the bright stair-rods. It was soothing to catch even that passing glimpse of a tranquil English home in the midst of the wild, dark business which had absorbed us.' *(Chapter 7)*

- 'In the uncertain, shadowy light I could see dimly that there were glancing, glimmering eyes peeping down at us from every cranny and corner. Even the rafters above our heads were lined by solemn fowls, who lazily shifted their weight from one leg to the other as our voices disturbed their slumbers.' *(Chapter 7)*

a) What location is being described?

----

b) How does this passage add to the atmosphere and mystery of the novel?

----

c) What is the effect of each of the highlighted phrases?

Sense of place: Locations

Activity 20

Another way that Conan Doyle creates a sense of place is by evoking the various geographical areas in which the action occurs. Look at the descriptions below and then match them with the correct location.

'The yellow glare from the shop-windows streamed out into the steamy, vaporous air and threw a murky, shifting radiance across the crowded thoroughfare. There was, to my mind, something eerie and ghost-like in the endless procession of faces which flitted across these narrow bars of light...' *(Chapter 3)*

'We had indeed reached a questionable and forbidding neighbourhood. Long lines of dull brick houses were only relieved by the coarse glare and tawdry brilliancy of public-houses at the corner. Then came rows of two-storeyed villas, each with a fronting of miniature garden, and then again interminable lines of new, staring brick buildings – the monster tentacles which the giant city was throwing out into the country.' *(Chapter 3)*

'...a great place, swarming with fanatics and fierce devil-worshippers of all sorts...It is all full of great deserted halls, and winding passages, and long corridors twisting in and out, so that it is easy enough for folk to get lost in it.' *(Chapter 12)*

A busy London street   The city of Agra   A London suburb

Activity 21

Annotate each of the highlighted phrases with your ideas about how this use of language is effective. In your notebook, write down your analysis in complete sentences.

Here is an example from one student:

The use of the image 'monster tentacles' makes it sound like the suburbs are part of a powerful octopus devouring the countryside and replacing it with something unpleasant and frightening.

Pathetic fallacy

Within his descriptions, there are many instances when Conan Doyle uses **pathetic fallacy** to reflect the emotional state of the characters and intensify the atmosphere.

> **pathetic fallacy** the assigning of human emotions to aspects of nature

Activity 22

Complete the table below with your analysis of these examples of pathetic fallacy.

"See how the yellow fog swirls down the street and drifts across the dun-coloured houses. What could be more hopelessly prosaic and material?" *(Chapter 1)*	Holmes uses the dull weather as an excuse for his own boredom and impatience. 'Dun' is a dull, dingy colour and symbolizes the ordinary and conventional society against which he is rebelling. He accuses the weather and his surroundings of being 'prosaic' as if they are at fault for lacking the imagination and excitement for which he yearns.
'...the dull heavy evening, with the strange business upon which we were engaged, combined to make me nervous and depressed.' *(Chapter 3)*	
'The east had been gradually whitening, and we could now see some distance in the cold grey light...The whole place, with its scattered dirt-heaps and ill-grown shrubs, had a blighted, ill-omened look which harmonized with the black tragedy which hung over it.' *(Chapter 7)*	
"The rain was still falling steadily, for it was just the beginning of the wet season. Brown, heavy clouds were drifting across the sky, and it was hard to see more than a stone-cast...It was strange to me to be standing there...waiting for the man who was coming to his death." *(Chapter 12)*	

Personification

Another type of imagery used by Conan Doyle is **personification**.

> **personification** when human qualities are given to something non-human, such as an object or an idea

Activity 23

Look at the examples below and then write a sentence for each one, explaining how the use of personification makes the image more vivid and interesting.

'Now the red rim of the sun pushes itself over the London cloudbank…' *(Chapter 7)*

'The square, massive house…towered up, sad and forlorn, behind us.' *(Chapter 7)*

"And yet, I have made no use of it myself, so blind and foolish a thing is avarice." *(Chapter 4)*

Activity 24

In order to write well about language you must have a confident grasp of literary terminology. To test your understanding match each literary term to the example from the novel:

Simile	"Lor' bless you, sir, he is that, and forward" *(Chapter 8)*
Metaphor	"they will instantly shut up like an oyster" *(Chapter 8)*
Pathetic fallacy	'Moonlight was streaming into the room, and it was bright with a vague and shifty radiance.' *(Chapter 5)*
Sociolect	"quick succession of strange surprises" *(Chapter 6)*
Sarcasm	'…such a disreputable little scarecrow' *(Chapter 8)*
Alliteration	"Then I shall study the great Jones's methods…" *(Chapter 6)*

Comic relief

> **comic relief** amusing or light-hearted episodes that provide a break from or contrast to more serious aspects

Activity 25

Read this student's response below. Put a tick next to any well-made points and then write a second paragraph to complete the answer in your notebook.

> How does Conan Doyle use comic relief in the novel?

Although this is a detective novel and has many serious, tense interludes, Conan Doyle also uses comic relief to lighten the mood and add variation. One example of this is the introduction of the dog Toby in Chapter 7. He is described humorously as having a 'clumsy, waddling gait' and yet Toby is surprisingly elegant when identifying a scent, described with the simile, 'like a connoisseur sniffing the bouquet of a famous vintage.' It is comic that such expertise comes from such an unlikely source.

Progress check

Use the chart below to review the skills you have developed in this chapter. For each column, start at the bottom box and work your way up towards the highest level in the top box. Tick the box to show you have achieved that level.

Language, structure, form	Technical accuracy
I can analyse the effects of Conan Doyle's use of language, structure and form in *The Sign of Four*, using subject terms judiciously ☐	I use a wide range of vocabulary and can spell and punctuate consistently accurately ☐
I can explain how Conan Doyle uses language, structure and form to create effects in *The Sign of Four*, using relevant subject terms ☐	I use a range of vocabulary and can spell and punctuate, mostly accurately ☐
I can identify some of Conan Doyle's methods in *The Sign of Four* and use some subject terms ☐	I use a simple range of vocabulary and spell and punctuate with some accuracy ☐

Language, structure, form

Technical accuracy

Themes

Crime

Two of the major crimes described in the novel are the murder of the rajah's servant (who travelled under the name of 'Achmet') and the murder of Bartholomew Sholto, in both cases murdered in order to steal the rajah's treasure.

Activity 1

Add to the spider diagrams below by collecting more information about the two crimes.

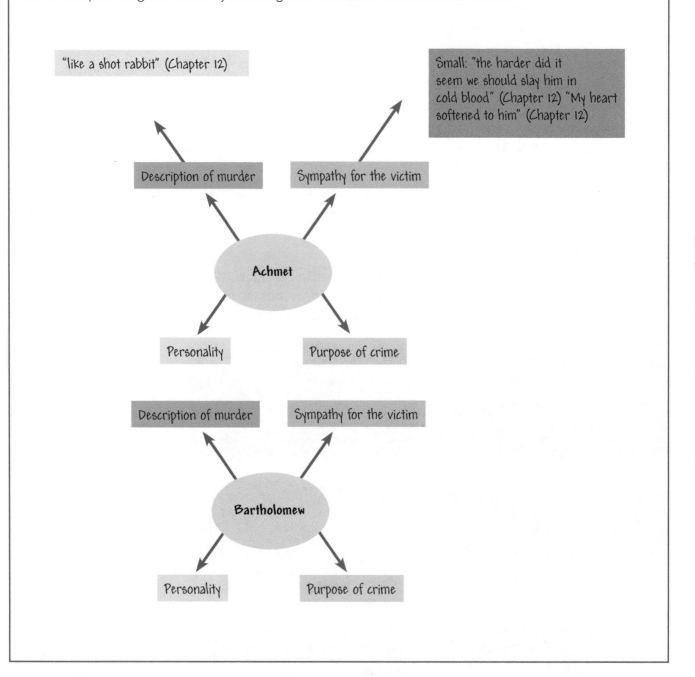

"like a shot rabbit" (Chapter 12)

Small: "the harder did it seem we should slay him in cold blood" (Chapter 12) "My heart softened to him" (Chapter 12)

Description of murder

Sympathy for the victim

Achmet

Personality

Purpose of crime

Description of murder

Sympathy for the victim

Bartholomew

Personality

Purpose of crime

Activity 2

In your notebook, write 250 words comparing how the theme of crime is presented in these two murders.

Punishment

Complete the table below detailing the punishments that various characters in the novel receive and why.

Character	Why they are punished	How they are punished	Key quotations
Jonathan Small	Punished for joining the 'Four' who kill and steal from Achmet. Punished for the death of Bartholomew Sholto. Theft of the treasure.		
Tonga		Shot by Watson and Holmes and disappears into the river.	
Major Sholto			"The cursed greed which has been my besetting sin..." (Chapter 4)
Bartholomew Sholto			'a horrible smile, a fixed and unnatural grin' (Chapter 5)
Captain Morstan		Heart attack during a quarrel with Sholto over the treasure.	

Revenge

Activity 4

Small claims that his chief motivation upon returning to England is to seek vengeance upon Major Sholto for his betrayal. Below are a few of Small's statements from Chapter 12.

"From that time I lived only for vengeance. I thought of it by day and I nursed it by night."

"To escape, to track down Sholto, to have my hand upon his throat – that was my one thought."

"A hundred times I have killed him in my sleep."

Do you believe that Small's quest for revenge is presented sympathetically or critically by Conan Doyle? Make a bullet point list of examples of how Small's version of his actions show to what extent he is justified in taking his actions.

Justice

Two types of justice are presented in the story: moral and legal justice.
For example, Thaddeus feels a great moral obligation to restore a share of the treasure to Morstan's heir, even though it could be argued that it should legally be returned to the rajah.

Key quotations

"I cared nothing for the law – nothing for the gallows." *(Chapter 12)*

"...I believe the best defence I can make is just to hold back nothing, but let all the world know how badly I have myself been served by Major Sholto, and how innocent I am of the death of his son." *(Chapter 12)*

Activity 5

Do you believe that at the end of the novel justice has been done? Write a paragraph, stating your opinion.

Love

The love between Mary Morstan and Watson is the sub-plot of the novel and, like the mystery that Holmes must solve, it begins in the second chapter and is resolved in the final chapter.

Activity 6

Read the following excerpt from Chapter 12 and then answer the questions below.

> "Well, and there is the end of our little drama," I remarked, after we had sat some time smoking in silence. "I fear that it may be the last investigation in which I shall have the chance of studying your methods. Miss Morstan has done me the honour to accept me as a husband in prospective."
>
> He gave a most dismal groan.
>
> "I feared as much," said he. "I really cannot congratulate you."
>
> I was a little hurt.
>
> "Have you any reason to be dissatisfied with my choice?" I asked.
>
> "Not at all, I think she is one of the most charming young ladies I ever met and might have been most useful in such work as we have been doing. She had a decided genius that way; witness the way in which she preserved that Agra plan from all the other papers of her father. But love is an emotional thing, and whatever is emotional is opposed to that true cold reason which I place above all things. I should never marry myself, lest I bias my judgment."
>
> "I trust," said I, laughing, "that my judgment may survive the ordeal. But you look weary." *(Chapter 12)*

a) What does the first paragraph suggest about Watson's attitude towards love?

----

b) What does Holmes's reaction suggest about his attitude towards love and marriage?

----

c) How does Holmes's statement that "love is an emotional thing, and whatever is emotional is opposed to that true cold reason which I place above all things" point out one of the key differences between Watson and Holmes?

Friendship

A number of different friendships of varying degrees of intensity, **reciprocity** and affection are depicted in the novel.

reciprocity mutual exchange; when something is returned in equal measure

Activity 7

Complete the table below.

Friendship between...	Positive aspects	Negative aspects	Key quotations
Holmes and Watson	Holmes and Watson have the adventures that both crave.	Watson is sometimes hurt by Holmes's lack of sensitivity.	
Small and Tonga	They are loyal to each other.		
Major Sholto and Captain Morstan			'paroxysm of anger' (Chapter 4)
Mary and Mrs Forrester		Not an equal relationship – as kind as she is, Mrs Forrester is Mary's employer.	

Activity 8

In your notebook, make a bullet point plan to prepare an answer to the following question:

'It could be said that the convict Jonathan Small, as demonstrated by his attitude towards loyalty and friendship, is a more honourable man than Major Sholto.'
To what extent do you agree with this statement?

Which friendship?

Activity 9

Look at the quotations below and decide which relationship is being described.

"Very much surprised was he when I made at him with the rope's end and cursed him for a little bloodthirsty imp." *(Chapter 12)*

_____ and _____

"He was staunch and true…" *(Chapter 12)*

_____ and _____

"They were bosom friends, those two, and never far apart." *(Chapter 12)*

_____ and _____

"Only one [friend] that we know of…" *(Chapter 2)*

_____ and _____

"Just sit in the corner there, that your footprints may not complicate matters." *(Chapter 6)*

_____ and _____

'…the two graceful, clinging figures…' *(Chapter 7)*

_____ and _____

Activity 10

A student has been asked to write a response to the following question:

> How does Conan Doyle present friendships in *The Sign of Four*?

To prepare, the student has begun making a plan but has left some unfinished sections. Complete the plan and add any additional ideas you may have.

Paragraph 1: The importance of Holmes and Watson's friendship based on contrasting personalities.	
Paragraph 2: Contrast with friendship of Jonathan Small and Tonga.	
Paragraph 3: Contrast language used to describe male friendships and female friendships.	Example: Language used to describe Major Sholto and Captain Morstan's friendship Example: Language used to describe Mrs Forrester and Mary's friendship
Paragraph 4: Importance to the plot and moral/ message of novel.	

Wealth and treasure

The pursuit of wealth is a theme of the novel and the source of the mystery.
There are the tangible signs of wealth, such as the fine pearls sent to Mary, the Agra treasure and Thaddeus's artistic treasures. There is also Mary who is presented as a metaphoric 'treasure' by Watson when he exults after winning her love.

Activity 11

Complete the table below to show how different treasures affect various characters.

Treasure	Description	How characters react to it	Importance to plot
Pearl	"rare variety and of considerable value" (Chapter 2) 'six of the finest pearls that I had ever seen.' (Chapter 2)		
Thaddeus's house	'The richest and glossiest of curtains...richly-mounted painting.' (Chapter 4)		
The Agra treasure		So tempting it is repeatedly stolen.	It is almost as if it is cursed – those who possess it come to a bad end, whereas Mary is relieved not to have it. She instead finds happiness with Watson.
Mary Morstan			

Follow the treasure

Activity 12

Complete the flow chart below showing the journey of the Agra treasure in the novel and what happens to everyone who possesses it.

a) Achmet

What happens?

b) ------------

What happens?

c) Major Sholto

What happens?

d) -----------

What happens?

e) Small and Tonga

What happens?

Activity 13

Complete the sentence below:

The journey of the treasure suggests that wealth does not necessarily bring happiness because

Wealth and social standing

Money is mentioned many times in the novel, from Mrs Smith's son asking for two shillings to the life-changing worth of the Agra treasure. Watson keenly feels his lack of wealth while Thaddeus ostentatiously displays his wealth, but only within the confines of his externally modest home.

Activity 14

a) Number the characters below in order of how wealthy you think they are:

Mr and Mrs Smith   -------   Mrs Cecil Forrester   -------   Bartholomew Sholto   -------

Jonathan Small   -------   Sherlock Holmes   -------   Dr Watson   -------

Mary Morstan   -------   Thaddeus Sholto   -------

The rajah   -------   Wiggins   -------

b) For each character listed, find a quotation that supports your idea about their wealth and attitude towards money. Below are a few quotations to get you started.

"I may call myself a patron of the arts." *(Chapter 4)*

"The pearls were evidently of great value, and he was averse to part with them, for between friends, my brother was himself a little inclined to my father's fault." *(Chapter 4)*

"Just imagine what it must be to be so rich, and to have the world at your feet!" *(Chapter 9)*

"…how my folk would stare when they saw their ne'er-do-weel coming back with his pockets full of gold moidores." *(Chapter 12)*

"Because this treasure, these riches, sealed my lips." *(Chapter 11)*

"Much has come to him from his father, and more still he has set by himself, for he is of a low nature and hoards his gold rather than spend it." *(Chapter 4)*

Englishness and foreignness

Most of the novel is set in London or its suburbs, but, in Chapter 12, the action suddenly moves to India, where Jonathan Small had been sent as a member of an army regiment.

Activity 15

Look at the words and phrases below and label each to indicate whether they describe England or India. How can you tell?

"half eaten by jackals and native dogs" (Chapter 12) _ _ _ _ _ _ _ _ _ _ _ _ _ _ _

'...stained glass, the barometer, and the bright stair-rods.'

(Chapter 7) _ _ _ _ _ _ _ _ _ _ _ _ _ _ _

'Down the Strand the lamps were but misty splotches of diffused

light...' (Chapter 3) _ _ _ _ _ _ _ _ _ _ _ _ _ _ _

"...a dreary fever-stricken place" (Chapter 12) _ _ _ _ _ _ _ _ _ _ _ _ _ _ _

Activity 16

Read the beginning of a student's essay comparing the depiction of England and India in the novel and then write at least three sentences completing it.

In 'The Sign of Four', India is presented as a rough, changeable place where a man might equally make his fortune or meet his death. Jonathan Small dreams of returning to his rural home in Worcestershire with his pockets full of foreign treasure ('gold moidores'). Although he knows what he is doing is wrong, he also indicates that he feels the rules of law are different in a place where he feels he could meet 'death at every turn'. His extreme adventures, his simple 'rover' beginning and his years of hardship have made him susceptible to the temptation of the treasure.

On the other hand, England is presented as

_ _

_ _

_ _

_ _

Duality

At the end of the novel, Holmes quotes the German writer Goethe lamenting that he cannot be two men: a good man and a rascal. This is one of many examples from the novel in which **duality** is explored.

> **doppelganger**
> a surprising double of a person
>
> **duality** being made up of two opposing parts, such as good and evil

Activity 17

Complete the table below by identifying all the positive and negative aspects of Holmes's character.

Positive aspects of Holmes's character	Negative aspects of Holmes's character
Brilliance	Drug use
Ability to solve crimes	Lack of empathy

The twins Bartholomew and Thaddeus could also be said to represent two sides of the same person: their appearance is identical, but their morality and motivations are very different. The concept of a good twin and an evil twin or **doppelgangers** is a common one in literature. In *The Strange Case of Dr Jekyll and Mr Hyde* (1886), Robert Louis Stevenson writes, 'Man is not truly one, but truly two.' Similarly, authors from Mary Shelley to Edgar Allan Poe explore the idea of the protagonist having a shadow character who follows and plagues them, exposing either the dark side of their character or of society.

Activity 18

Read the statement below and, in your notebook, write your response to the following question:

> 'Some feel that the hypocrisy and repression of the Victorian age heightened the interest in stories where good and evil exist together in close proximity.' To what extent do you believe this applies to the novel *The Sign of Four*? Consider how the context and language of the novel explore the theme of duality.

Emotion versus rationality

Conan Doyle displays an active interest in the scientific and philosophical arguments of his age. Watson and Holmes engage in a number of discussions about logic, emotion and the nature of existence.

Activity 19

Read the excerpt from Chapter 10 and then answer the questions below.

> based on deduction rather than personal experience

> "Dirty-looking rascals, but I suppose every one has some little immortal spark concealed about him. You would not think it, to look at them. There is no *a priori* probability about it. A strange enigma is man!"
>
> "Someone calls him a soul concealed in an animal," I suggested.
>
> "Winwood Reade is good upon the subject," said Holmes. "He remarks that, while the individual man is an insoluble puzzle, in the aggregate he becomes a mathematical certainty. You can, for example, never foretell what any one man will do, but you can say with precision what an average number will be up to. Individuals vary, but percentages remain constant. So says the statistician." *(Chapter 10)*

> something that is hard to understand, mysterious

a) What is Holmes's observation about the 'Dirty-looking rascals'?

----

b) What do you think the phrase 'a soul concealed in an animal' means?

----

c) How does this interest in 'mathematical certainty' relate to the way Holmes reasons?

----

d) What would appeal to Holmes about Reade's ideas?

Which theme?

Activity 20

Look at the quotations and incidents from the novel listed below. Which theme (or themes) do you think each quotation or incident could be used to exemplify?

Holmes's deduction based on Watson's brother's watch *(Chapter 1)*

- - - - - - - - - - - - - - -

'She has told me since that she thought me cold and distant upon that journey. She little guessed the struggle within my breast, or the effort of self-restraint which held me back.' *(Chapter 7)*

- - - - - - - - - - - - - - - -

"Because I love you, Mary, as truly as ever a man loved a woman." *(Chapter 11)*

- - - - - - - - - - - - - - - -

The newspaper account announcing Jones's arrest of various members of the Sholto household *(Chapter 8)*

- - - - - - - - - - - - - - -

Sherlock Holmes's analysis of the crime scene compared to Jones's *(Chapter 6)*

- - - - - - - - - - - - -

"It is my treasure, and if I can't have the loot I'll take darned good care that no one else does." *(Chapter 12)*

- - - - - - - - - - - - - - -

Activity 21

Now find at least three additional incidents or quotations that could support each of the themes. Write these in your notebook.

Upgrade

A theme should be reinforced by events and quotations that occur several times throughout the novel. Ensure that you are aware of how each theme develops throughout the novel.

Theme development

When discussing a theme, you should be able to refer to several incidents that will demonstrate either different aspects of the theme or how the reader's understanding of the theme may deepen as the novel progresses.

Opposite is an example of the development of the theme of **wealth and treasure**.

First mention

The pearls: At first, obtaining the treasure seems desirable.

Example 1

The Agra treasure (Sholtos): Has caused fear and death, disrupted and haunted their lives.

Example 2

The Agra treasure (The Four/Morstan/Sholto): Tempts characters to break law. Is the source of loyalty between the Four, but causes Morstan and Sholto to fall out.

Example 3

The Agra treasure (Mary): Relief when it is gone. Shows her values.

Conclusion

Pursuit of ill-gotten gains only causes sorrow.

Progress check

Use the chart below to review the skills you have developed in this chapter.
For each column, start at the bottom box and work your way up towards the
highest level in the top box. Tick the box to show you have achieved that level.

I can sustain a critical response to *The Sign of Four* and interpret the themes convincingly ☐

I can use well-integrated textual references from *The Sign of Four* to support my interpretation ☐

I can develop a coherent response to *The Sign of Four* and explain the themes clearly ☐

I can use quotations and other textual references from *The Sign of Four* to support my explanation ☐

I can make some comments on the themes in *The Sign of Four* ☐

I can make references to some details from *The Sign of Four* ☐

Personal response

Textual references

Skills and Practice

Understanding questions

Make sure that you read the question carefully in your assessment. It is important that you understand what the focus of the question is and which theme, character and language analysis is required.

Activity 1

Read the questions below and underline the key words (the first has been done for you).

a) <u>How</u> does Conan Doyle use <u>language</u> to create a sense of <u>atmosphere</u> and place?

b) Choose two friendships in the novel and compare and contrast how they are presented.

c) To what extent is Jonathan Small portrayed as the villain of the novel?

d) How is the theme of love developed in the novel?

e) How are the attitudes and feelings of Mary Morstan explored in the novel?

f) How is the relationship between Holmes and Watson presented?

g) What literary techniques does Conan Doyle use to create a sense of suspense and mystery?

Writing your own questions

Activity 2

Using the questions above as models, try to write your own questions for each of the following topics:

- Character: --

- Theme: --

- Relationships: --

- Setting: --

- Language: --

Planning your answers

| **Step 1** | Identify the key words in the question. |

↓

| **Step 2** | Decide on some main headings that are relevant to the key words. |

↓

| **Step 3** | Jot down your ideas under the headings, for example in a spider diagram. |

↓

| **Step 4** | Organize your ideas into a paragraph plan for an essay. |

Activity 3

Plan your answer to the following question in your notebook:

How are the attitudes and feelings of Mary Morstan explored in the novel?

a) **Step 1** Underline the key words in the question that tell you what you are being asked to do.

b) **Step 2** Add your own headings to the spider diagram below.

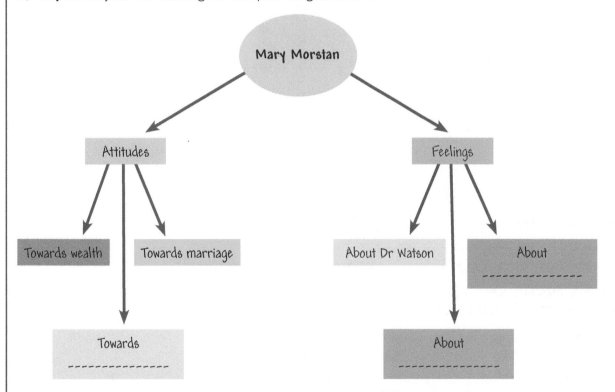

c) **Step 3** For each heading in the spider diagram, jot down your ideas in your notebook. Include notes about what evidence from the novel you will use to support each idea.

d) **Step 4** Create a five-paragraph essay plan. Ensure that you have clear examples from the novel and are able to write about the language, structure and context. Remember to use correct literary terminology.

Revision task: Character cards

Activity 4

Use the headings below to create revision cards to prepare for your assessment.

Character:

- -

Importance to plot:

- -

- -

- -

Connection to themes:

- -

- -

Key quotations:

- -

- -

- -

One has been done for you:

Character: Athelney Jones

Importance to plot: The conventional, paid detective contrasts with the gentleman-at-leisure Holmes. Arrests Thaddeus. Emphasizes how brilliant Holmes is.

Connection to themes: Rationality (he lacks it, jumps to false conclusions); crime and punishment (ultimately the one to take Small away for conventional justice).

Key quotations: "more by good luck than guidance" (Chapter 6); "You see that I am weaving my web round Thaddeus" (Chapter 6); "duty is duty…I shall feel more at ease when we have our story-teller here safe under lock and key" (Chapter 12).

Use the cards to memorize key quotations relevant to each character and to remind yourself of his or her importance to the plot.

Revision task: Location chart

Activity 5

Complete the table below to revise key ideas and quotations about the main locations in the novel.

Location	Chapter(s)	Importance to plot/theme	Key language features/ quotation
Thaddeus Sholto's home	4	English/foreign; connects England to the more exotic locations of the last chapter; Aesthetic Movement – art for art's sake; contrast between exterior and interior.	
Pondicherry Lodge			
Baker Street			
The Agra Fort			
Mr Sherman's home			
Mrs Forrester's home			

Activity 6

Choose one of the locations above and complete the spider diagram below to prepare an answer to the following question:

How far is Conan Doyle's choice of locations vital to establishing atmosphere and a sense of mystery?

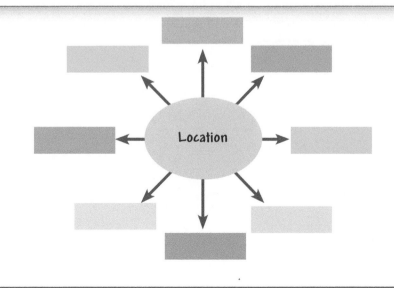

Using quotations

 Activity 7

The student's essay below includes quotations but they are far too long. In your notebook, rewrite the essay, choosing shorter quotations and embedding them correctly into the sentences.

> Conan Doyle presents two sides of Sherlock Holmes. At the novel's opening he is shown using drugs:
>
> > 'Sherlock Holmes took his bottle from the corner of the mantel-piece, and his hypodermic syringe from its neat morocco case. With his long, white, nervous fingers he adjusted the delicate needle and rolled back his left shirt-cuff. For some little time his eyes rested thoughtfully upon the sinewy forearm and wrist, all dotted and scarred with innumerable puncture-marks.' (Chapter 1)
>
> From this, it is clear that Holmes frequently uses drugs, which annoys Watson, who says that he has:
>
> > '...witnessed this performance, but custom had not reconciled my mind to it. On the contrary, from day to day I had become more irritable at the sight...' (Chapter 1)
>
> However, on the other hand, Watson clearly admires Holmes because he writes:
>
> > 'His great powers, his masterly manner, and the experience which I had had of his many extraordinary qualities, all made me diffident and backward in crossing him.' (Chapter 1)
>
> Throughout the novel there is a tension between the positive and negative aspects of Holmes.

Upgrade

Use short, well-chosen quotations and embed them in a grammatically correct way into your sentences. For example, 'Holmes can be excellent company when he "chooses", such as when he is "brilliant", and displays his "bright humour" at the dinner with Jones and Watson.'

Point, Evidence, Explanation (PEE)

Examiners will be looking for students who can support their ideas with evidence from the text and the ability to analyse these examples. This technique is sometimes called Point, Evidence, Explanation (PEE).

Activity 8

The student below has several points they wish to make, but, in some cases, has been unable to find evidence from the text or to explain the quotations and how they support the points. Complete the plan by providing evidence and explanations where missing.

Point: Mary Morstan is portrayed sympathetically as an intelligent, appealing and sensible person who has not always had an easy life.

Evidence: Watson declares that she is a 'very attractive woman' and Holmes says she is a "most charming"' young lady with a "decided genius".

Explanation: Mary Morstan's positive qualities are heightened both by Watson's immediate positive reaction and the reserved approval of the difficult-to-please Holmes.

Point: Mary Morstan is unable to take a fully active role in the solving of the mystery.

Evidence: _____

Explanation: _____

Point: Mary Morstan is shown to be a moral person with clear priorities.

Evidence: _____

Explanation: _____

Point: Mary Morstan and Watson are well matched as a couple.

Evidence: _____

Explanation: _____

If, when you are checking over your essay, you discover a number of paragraphs ending with quotations, that may be a sign that you are forgetting to analyse your evidence.

Organizing your ideas

Using discursive markers

To increase the sophistication of your writing and to demonstrate your ability to order and prioritize your ideas, you should use **discursive markers**.

> **discursive marker**
> a 'signpost' word or phrase that helps to direct the reader to the order, importance or relationship of ideas being presented

Examples of discursive markers for essays

Ordering

First

Second

Finally

Subsequently

In the beginning

At the end

Next

Emphasizing/Prioritizing

Most importantly

Significantly

Especially

Importantly

Notably

In particular

Relationship/Comparisons/Contrasts

Similarly

In contrast

Likewise

In the same way

Equally

On the other hand

Conversely

Alternatively

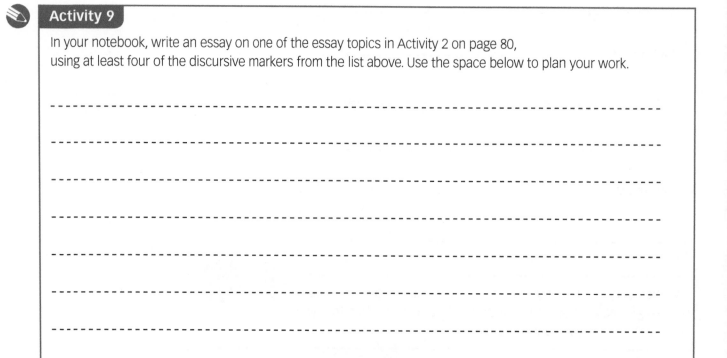

Activity 9

In your notebook, write an essay on one of the essay topics in Activity 2 on page 80, using at least four of the discursive markers from the list above. Use the space below to plan your work.

Sample question 1

Activity 10

Starting with the extract from Chapter 10 below, explore the importance of Tonga to the plot and mystery of the novel.

What words does Conan Doyle use to make Tonga seem less human and more terrifying?

What words or phrases make Tonga seem exotic and inhuman?

What is Tonga planning to do?

How does Watson interpret Tonga's appearance as suggesting his personality?

How is Tonga's death described? How does this contribute to the mystery and plot?

'Holmes had already drawn his revolver, and I whipped out mine at the sight of this savage, distorted creature. He was wrapped in some sort of dark ulster or blanket, which left only his face exposed, but that face was enough to give a man a sleepless night. Never have I seen features so deeply marked with all bestiality and cruelty. His small eyes glowed and burned with a sombre light, and his thick lips were writhed back from his teeth, which grinned and chattered at us with half animal fury.

…It was well that we had so clear a view of him. Even as we looked he plucked out from under his covering a short, round piece of wood, like a school-ruler, and clapped it to his lips. Our pistols rang out together. He whirled round, threw up his arms, and, with a kind of choking cough, fell sideways into the stream. I caught one glimpse of his venomous, menacing eyes amid the white swirl of the waters. At the same moment the wooden-legged man threw himself upon the rudder and put it hard down, so that his boat made straight for the southern bank, while we shot past her stern, only clearing her by a few feet. We were round after her in an instant, but she was already nearly at the bank.' *(Chapter 10)*

Before answering the questions below, take note of the close reading questions in the margins.

a) How is Tonga portrayed in the excerpt above?

b) How does Tonga contribute to the mystery and plot of the novel?
Remember to consider the context in which the novel was written.

Sample question 2

Activity 11

> How is love in Victorian England portrayed in the novel?

Read the extract below from Chapter 11 and use it as the starting point for answering the question above.

> "The treasure is lost," said Miss Morstan calmly.
>
> As I listened to the words and realized what they meant, a great shadow seemed to pass from my soul. I did not know how this Agra treasure had weighed me down, until now that it was finally removed. It was selfish, no doubt, disloyal, wrong, but I could realize nothing save that the golden barrier was gone from between us.
>
> "Thank God!" I ejaculated from my very heart.
>
> She looked at me with a quick, questioning smile.
>
> "Why do you say that?" she asked.
>
> "Because you are within my reach again," I said, taking her hand. She did not withdraw it. "Because I love you, Mary, as truly as ever a man loved a woman. Because this treasure, these riches, sealed my lips. Now that they are gone I can tell you how I love you. That is why I said, 'Thank God'."
>
> "Then I say 'Thank God', too," she whispered, as I drew her to my side.
>
> Whoever had lost a treasure, I knew that night that I had gained one.
> *(Chapter 11)*

Before writing your response, consider the following discussion points:

- Why has the treasure previously been a barrier to their romance?
- What is surprising about Mary's reaction and what does this tell the reader about her character?
- What actions do the characters take that might be considered stereotypically feminine or masculine?
- To what is Mary metaphorically compared?

Sample question 3

Activity 12

Read the following extract from Chapter 4 and then answer both of the questions below, using the additional questions in the margins to assist you.

> "When I first determined to make this communication to you," said he, "I might have given you my address; but I feared that you might disregard my request and bring unpleasant people with you. I took the liberty, therefore, of making an appointment in such a way that my man Williams might be able to see you first. I have complete confidence in his discretion, and he had orders, if he were dissatisfied, to proceed no further in the matter. You will excuse these precautions, but I am a man of somewhat retiring, and I might even say refined, tastes, and there is nothing more unaesthetic than a policeman. I have a natural shrinking from all forms of rough materialism. I seldom come in contact with the rough crowd. I live, as you see, with some little atmosphere of elegance around me. I may call myself a patron of the arts. It is my weakness. The landscape is a genuine Corot, and though a connoisseur might perhaps throw a doubt upon that Salvator Rosa, there cannot be the least question about the Bouguereau. I am partial to the modern French school."
>
> "You will excuse me, Mr Sholto," said Miss Morstan, "but I am here at your request to learn something which you desire to tell me. It is very late, and I should desire the interview to be as short as possible." *(Chapter 4)*

Margin questions:

- What does Thaddeus's fear of 'unpleasant people' suggest?
- What does this tell the reader about Thaddeus's reliance on Williams?
- What is humorous about this?
- What does this tell the reader about how Thaddeus lives?
- What does this tell the reader about Thaddeus's interests?
- What is Mary Morstan's reaction to Thaddeus at this point?

a) How is the character of Thaddeus Sholto presented in this extract?

b) What is Thaddeus Sholto's importance in the novel as a whole?

Sample question 4

Activity 13

Read the excerpt below from Chapter 12 and then answer the two questions below. Remember to refer to the novel's context, language and structure.

"Justice!" snarled the ex-convict. "A pretty justice! Whose loot is this, if it is not ours? Where is the justice that I should give it up to those who have never earned it? Look how I have earned it! Twenty long years in that fever-ridden swamp, all day at work under the mangrove-tree, all night chained up in the filthy convict-huts, bitten by mosquitoes, racked with ague, bullied by every cursed black-faced policeman who loved to take it out of a white man. That was how I earned the Agra treasure, and you talk to me of justice because I cannot bear to feel that I have paid this price only that another may enjoy it! I would rather swing a score of times, or have one of Tonga's darts in my hide, than live in a convict's cell and feel that another man is at his ease in a palace with the money that should be mine." *(Chapter 12)*

a) How is the theme of crime and punishment portrayed in this excerpt?

b) How is the theme of crime and punishment depicted in the rest of the novel?

Activity 14

Here is one student's plan to answer the question above. In your notebook, complete the plan by adding more detail or different points.

1. Introduction: Small – the criminal who is being pursued by Holmes. In Chapter 12 tells his side of the story.

2. Language: Exclamation marks – show he is angry. Emotive language: 'racked', 'bullied'. Emphasizes his ordeal and the foreignness of his experience. 'Tonga's dart', 'fever-ridden swamp'.

3. Context: Different sense of justice in foreign setting. Colonies as a source of wealth, sometimes ill-gotten.

4. Structure: The novel is structured to bring Small to justice.

5. Other instances of crime and punishment: Is justice done?

6. Conclusion: Attitude towards Small at end of novel. How will he be punished?

Sample essay 1

Activity 15

Read the opening of the sample student essay below and underline every example
of literary terminology used in it.

> How does Conan Doyle use <u>language</u> to create a sense of <u>suspense</u> and
> <u>horror</u> in Chapter 5?

Chapter 5 begins in a tense way, with the title 'The Tragedy of Pondicherry Lodge'
<u>foreshadowing</u> the horror to come. One source of suspense and tension is the night-time
setting. The 'damp fog' and the personification of the 'half a moon peeping occasionally'
increase the sense of dread. There is a momentary lightening of the tension with the
comic relief of McMurdo and his surprising prior knowledge of Sherlock Holmes and his
boxing career. However, the sense of dread returns with the description of the grounds,
which heightens the tension and suspense since the building seems particularly ominous
described by negative phrases like 'its deathly silence' and 'chill to the heart'. The
word 'deathly' prepares the reader for the horrific find in the locked room and 'chill'
emphasizes the terror the characters are feeling. Suspense is also created for the reader
as they are highly aware of the narrator Watson's reactions to his surroundings.

Activity 16

Then in your notebook:

a) create a plan to complete the essay

b) write three more paragraphs of the essay

c) underline any literary terminology you use.

Sample essay 2

Activity 17

Read through the essay below and note when the student has done any of the following:

- commented on language
- commented on context
- commented on structure
- referred specifically to the question.

> How is the theme of duality explored in the novel?

From the opening chapter the duality of Sherlock Holmes is portrayed. Watson expresses his frustration that someone with the 'great powers' and 'masterly manner' of Sherlock Holmes should waste his talents indulging in decadent habits such as taking drugs. However, Holmes is not the only example of duality. There are also two sides of Jonathan Small and, it could be argued, that the twins Thaddeus and Bartholomew Sholto form two distinct sides of the same person. It was also written in an age where there was a curiosity about what was hidden behind closed doors, so the discoveries in the two Sholto households also demonstrate a duality of what is hidden behind a deceptive exterior.

In the Victorian age, there was interest in the idea of duality, with a number of novels exploring the idea that a man might have both a good and an evil side. Holmes himself, at the novel's conclusion, quotes German lines by Goethe lamenting that it's a shame he can't be two men, a good man and a rascal. While Holmes, in the narrator Watson's view, is mainly an admirable figure, the convict Jonathan Small is a largely wicked character, who is treated with surprising sympathy at the novel's resolution.

One key chapter for exploring duality is Chapter 4, when there is the contrast between the 'commonplace doorway of a third-rate suburban dwelling-house' with the riches within, which are highlighted by the simile as looking 'as out of place as a diamond of the first water in a setting of brass'. This suggests that these riches are hidden by their cheap setting. In this chapter Conan Doyle has made clear the different personalities of the Sholto twins: the hypochondriac Thaddeus is generous and moral whereas 'Brother Bartholomew' wishes to keep the treasure for himself. The next chapter further explores a deceptive location: Pondicherry Lodge is an English home, but given an Indian name, suggesting the combination of English and foreign influences on the Sholto family.

Activity 18

Next, in your notebook, complete this essay, providing clear evidence from the novel.

Progress check

Use the chart below to review the skills you have developed in this chapter. For each column, start at the bottom box and work your way up towards the highest level in the top box. Tick the box to show you have achieved that level.

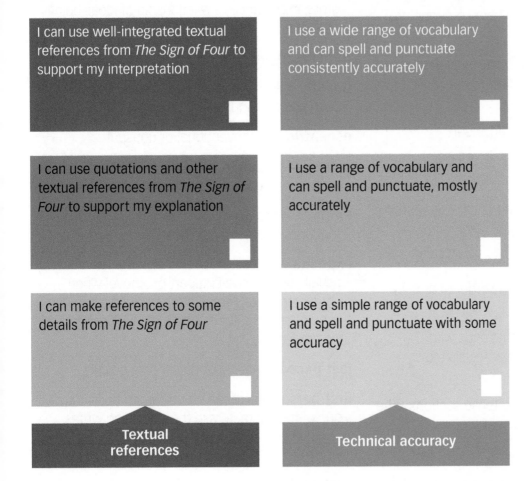

I can use well-integrated textual references from *The Sign of Four* to support my interpretation ☐

I use a wide range of vocabulary and can spell and punctuate consistently accurately ☐

I can use quotations and other textual references from *The Sign of Four* to support my explanation ☐

I use a range of vocabulary and can spell and punctuate, mostly accurately ☐

I can make references to some details from *The Sign of Four* ☐

I use a simple range of vocabulary and spell and punctuate with some accuracy ☐

Textual references

Technical accuracy

Glossary

Aesthetic Movement an arts movement in the latter half of the 19th century that promoted 'art for art's sake'. Followers favoured highly decorative objects and were often influenced by exotic artefacts from abroad being brought into Europe at the time

alliteration the use of the same first letter or sound in words that are next to one another or very closely grouped together

antagonist an opponent or adversary

anthropomorphism attributing human characteristics to an animal or object

anti-climactic less important or exciting than the build-up or climax that has just taken place

catalyst something that causes an event

chronological arranged in the order of time in which events occurred

circular structure a form that ends with phrasing or subject matter that recalls the beginning of the narrative

climax the most exciting and tense section of the novel, which usually occurs near the end

clue evidence used in the detection of crime

comic relief amusing or light-hearted episodes that provide a break from or contrast to more serious aspects

complication plot or character detail that makes a straightforward solution more difficult

conflict when characters have opposing desires or objectives

decadent in a state of moral decline; self-indulgent

denouement the final part of a novel when the various strands of the plot are brought together and resolved

dialect particular pronunciations and word choices used by people of a specific geographical region

dialogue the speeches or conversations in a book or play

diction choice of words

discursive marker a 'signpost' word or phrase that helps to direct the reader to the order, importance or relationship of ideas being presented

doppelganger a surprising double of a person

duality being made up of two opposing parts, such as good and evil

eccentric unconventional or unusual

emotive language words chosen to encourage a certain emotion like sorrow or pity

Empire a group of countries ruled over by a monarch or other single power

exposition description and explanation of ideas, usually used in the first part of a novel when characters and themes are introduced, but also used elsewhere, for example to give background information

fast-paced moving or developing quickly

first person narrator a narrator who is usually one of the characters in the novel and writes about events from a single perspective, using the word 'I'

flashback a narrative device in which the chronological order of the story is interrupted and events from an earlier time are presented

Gothic horror a genre of fiction that often revolves around a large, dark, frightening house and horrible secrets

heightened more elevated or intense

irony words that express the opposite of what is meant; the difference between what may be expected and what actually occurs; can also be used to make the reader or audience aware of something unknown to the characters

metaphor a comparison of one thing to another to make a description more vivid; unlike a simile, it does not use the words 'like' or 'as', but states that something is something else

narrator a person or character who tells a story

novel   a lengthy piece of prose fiction that usually uses character and action to convey its narrative

omniscient third person narrator   an all-knowing narrator who can relate the thoughts and feelings of many characters, usually in the third person

pathetic fallacy   the assigning of human emotions to aspects of nature

percussive   related to drumming or striking

personification   when human qualities are given to something non-human, such as an object or an idea

plot   the events or storyline of a narrative

protagonist   the central character in the novel

reciprocity   mutual exchange; when something is returned in equal measure

register   the choices of language dependent upon external factors such as occasion, audience and purpose

resolution   the point in the story where the mystery or problem of the story is solved or brought to a conclusion

sarcasm   type of irony, using words to mean the opposite of what is said, often creating either a comic or insulting effect

secular   non-religious, not associated with spiritual matters

sensational   designed to excite or interest

sibilant   a speech sound that has a hissing sound such as that produced by saying 's' or 'sh'

simile   a comparison of one thing to another, using 'like' or 'as'

sociolect   particular pronunciations and word choices used by people of a particular social class

staid   settled, unadventurous, conservative

stock character   easily recognized, familiar character that requires little development or insight

sub-plot   a second plot that runs alongside the main plot

suspense   a state of uncertainty, perhaps awaiting a judgement or solution

synecdoche   a figure of speech in which part of something is used to represent the whole, such as 'The ominous boots approached the door', meaning the soldiers who were wearing the boots

syntax   the structure of sentences, including word order and grammar

tension   elements that make the reader feel worried, interested, fearful or excited

unbiased   impartial and lacking in prejudice; even-handed

Great Clarendon Street, Oxford, OX2 6DP, United Kingdom

Oxford University Press is a department of the University of Oxford.
It furthers the University's objective of excellence in research, scholarship,
and education by publishing worldwide. Oxford is a registered trade mark
of Oxford University Press in the UK and in certain other countries

British Library Cataloguing in Publication Data

Data available

ISBN 978-0-19-839888-2

10 9 8 7 6 5 4 3 2 1

Printed in Great Britain by CPI Group (UK) Ltd., Croydon CR0 4YY

Acknowledgements

The publisher and authors would like the thank the following for
permission to use photographs and other copyright material:

Cover: Q44/Alamy Stock Photo, Shutterstock; **p25**: Gift of John D.
Rockefeller, Jr. and John D. Rockefeller III/Brooklyn Museum/Creative
Commons-BY.